INSTRUCTOR'S RESOURCE MANUAL
with Tests

Harry Nickla
Creighton University

ESSENTIALS OF GENETICS
Fifth Edition

William S. Klug
Michael R. Cummings

D1501820

PEARSON
Prentice
Hall

Upper Saddle River, NJ 07458

Editor-in-Chief, Science: John Challice
Executive Editor: Gary Carlson
Project Manager: Crissy Dudonis
Vice President of Production & Manufacturing: David W. Riccardi
Executive Managing Editor: Kathleen Schiaparelli
Assistant Managing Editor: Becca Richter
Production Editor: Rhonda Aversa
Supplement Cover Manager: Paul Gourhan
Supplement Cover Designer: Joanne Alexandris
Manufacturing Buyer: Ilene Kahn

© 2005 Pearson Education, Inc.
Pearson Prentice Hall
Pearson Education, Inc.
Upper Saddle River, NJ 07458

Pearson Prentice Hall® is a trademark of Pearson Education, Inc.

The author and publisher of this book have used their best efforts in preparing this book. These efforts include the development, research, and testing of the theories and programs to determine their effectiveness. The author and publisher make no warranty of any kind, expressed or implied, with regard to these programs or the documentation contained in this book. The author and publisher shall not be liable in any event for incidental or consequential damages in connection with, or arising out of, the furnishing, performance, or use of these programs.

Printed in the United States of America

10 9 8 7 6 5 4 3 2 1

ISBN 0-13-143511-6

Pearson Education Ltd., *London*
Pearson Education Australia Pty. Ltd., *Sydney*
Pearson Education Singapore, Pte. Ltd.
Pearson Education North Asia Ltd., *Hong Kong*
Pearson Education Canada, Inc., *Toronto*
Pearson Educación de Mexico, S.A. de C.V.
Pearson Education—Japan, *Tokyo*
Pearson Education Malaysia, Pte. Ltd.

Table of Contents

Supplemental Questions and Problems with Brief Answers

Essentials of Genetics (5th edition)

Preface

This Instructor's Resource Manual was written to accompany the 5th edition of *Essentials of Genetics* by William S. Klug and Michael R. Cummings. Its intent is to provide helpful information to instructors as they face the challenge of designing a course with a new text. This manual has three main sections: (1) audiovisual materials and laboratory kits, (2) careers in genetics, and (3) supplemental questions and problems with answers. Approximately 70 of the questions in the True/False section of each chapter were provided by Gyula Ficsor, Professor of Biomedical Sciences, Department of Biological Sciences, Western Michigan University. I would like to thank the able assistance of Kelly Fitzgerald in the preparation of this manual.

Instructors may also find the following supplements helpful. All are available from Prentice Hall.

Student Handbook: Outlines, Answers to All Text Questions, Sample Test Questions with Answers

Companion Website: Animated Tutorials, Practice Quizzes, Research Tools

New York Times Themes of the Times: *Genetics and Molecular Biology*

Instructor's CD-ROM containing
- All Animations from the Student CD-ROM
- Student Website Link
- All Art Figures from the Text
- PowerPoint™ format for figures
- The complete Instructor's Manual
- Glossary

Transparencies

Internet Resources

Stull, A., and H. Nickla. 2000. *Science on the Internet: A Student's Guide* 2000-2001. Prentice Hall, Upper Saddle River, NJ. 07458

The errors in this manual are mine and I request that users direct me to any errors they detect. Thank you.

Harry Nickla
Department of Biology
Creighton University
Omaha, Nebraska 68178
hnickla@creighton.edu
August, 2003

Audiovisual Materials

While there are a number of films, computer programs, and videos on the market, the following are especially useful for a course constructed around this genetics text.

Tape #	Title	Length	Source
1	Great Scientists Speak Again: Mendel	25 min.	Univ. of California Extension Media Center 2176 Shattuck Ave. Berkeley, CA 94704
2	The Genetic Gamble	58 min.	Coronet Film and Video 108 Wilmot Road Deerfield, IL 60015
3	Bacterial Transformation	15 min.	Taped Technologies P. O. Box 384 Logan, UT 84321
4	The Race for the Double Helix	2 hr.	BBC - New York Office (212) 581-7100 or: Films for the Humanities and Sciences, POBox 2053 Princeton, NJ 08543-2053 www.films.com
5	LifePatent Pending	57 min.	Time-Life Video 100 Eisenhower Dr. Paramus, NJ 07652
6	Decoding the Book of Life	58 min.	Coronet Film and Video 108 Wilmot Road Deerfield, IL 60015
7	Genetics: Patterns of Development	26 min.	Coronet Film and Video
8	Did Darwin Get it Wrong?	57 min.	Univ. Film and Video Univ. of Minnesota 1313 Fifth St. S.E. #108 Minneapolis, MN 55414
9	Rapid Isolation of Plasmid DNA	10 min.	Taped Technologies
10	Agarose Gel Electrophoresis	19 min.	Taped Technologies
11	48 Hours: Marked for Life	45 min.	Ambrose Video Publ. Co. 1290 Ave. of the Americas Suite 2245 New York, NY 10104
12	Translating the Code: Protein Synthesis	27 min.	Human Relations Media 175 Thompkins Ave. Pleasantville, NY 10570
13	Patterns of Genetics: Understanding Genetics	33 min.	Human Relations Media
14	A Question of Genes: Inherited Risks	106 min.	Films for the Humanities and Sciences, POBox 2053 Princeton, NJ 08543-2053 www.films.com
15	Cutting and Splicing DNA	26 min.	Films for the Humanities
16	After Darwin: Genetics, Eugenics, and the Human Genome	95 min.	Films for the Humanities

17	Biotechnology	23 min.	Films for the Humanities
18	DNA Profiling	15 min.	Films for the Humanities
19	Hand-Me-Down Genes: How Genes Work	25 min.	Films for the Humanities
	Family Patterns	28 min.	
20	Genetics: A Popular Guide to the Principles of Human Heredity (3 videos)		Films for the Humanities
	(a) Understanding the Basic Concepts of Genetics	30 min.	
	(b) Genetic Discoveries, Disorders and Mutations	26 min.	
	(c) Practical Applications and Risks of Genetic Science	24 min.	
21	Human Genes Decoded	31 min.	Films for the Humanities
22	Science, Society, and the Human Genome Project	46 min.	Films for the Humanities
23	A History of Gene Therapy	46 min.	Films for the Humanities
24	Footpath Murders: DNA Profiling's Landmark Case	24 min.	Films for the Humanities
25	Crime Scene: Advances in DNA Testing	55 min.	Films for the Humanities
26	The Science of Cloning	25 min.	Films for the Humanities
27	The Cloning Revolution	50 min.	Films for the Humanities
28	Cloning: Miracle or Mistake?	20 min.	Films for the Humanities
29	Why Not Clone a Human? Ethical Challenges of Biotechnology	45 min.	Films for the Humanities
30	Spares or Repairs: Applications and Implications of Cloning	26 min.	Films for the Humanities
31	Growing Human Organs	26 min.	Films for the Humanities
32	Voyage Inside the Cell	15 min.	Films for the Humanities
33	Apoptosis: Cell Death and Cancer	51 min	Films for the Humanities
34	Programmed Death of a Cell	30 min.	Films for the Humanities
35	Bacteria and Viruses	20 min.	Films for the Humanities
36	Cell Wars: How the Immune System...	26 min.	Films for the Humanities
37	Superbugs: When Antibiotics Don't Work	45 min.	Films for the Humanities
38	A History of Antibiotics	47 min.	Films for the Humanities
39	Viruses: Conquering an Invisible World	52 min.	Films for the Humanities
40	The Emerging Viruses	50 min.	Films for the Humanities
41	Our Immune System	23 min.	Films for the Humanities
42	Molecular Biology	42 min.	Films for the Humanities
43	AIDS	35 min.	Films for the Humanities
44	Cancer and Metastasis	39 min.	Films for the Humanities
45	DNA	50 min	Teacher's Video Company POBox ASCA-4455 Scottsdale, AZ 85261 1-800-262-8837
46	Chromosomes and Genes	30 min.	Teacher's Video Company
47	Web of Life	58 min.	Teacher's Video Company
48	Heredity: Health Quiz	30 min.	Teacher's Video Company
49	Sheep Have Been Cloned	50 min.	Teacher's Video Company
50	Bioterror	60 min.	NOVA: WGBH Boston Video 1-800-949-8670

Sources for Purchase/Rental of Interactive and Descriptive Software, Films, Videotapes, and CD-ROMs

All Biological/Science Topics

CyberED, Inc. (CDs Multimedia)
P.O. Box 3480
(888)318-0700
Chico, CA 95927-3480
http://www.cybered.net

FFI (Films for the Humanities and Sciences)
(Videos, CD-ROMs)
P.O. Box 2053, Princeton, NJ 08543-2053
(800) 257-5126
e-mail: custserv@films.com
http://www.films.com

Hawkhill Associates
(Videos)
125 East Gilman St., P.O. Box 1029, Madison, WI
53701-1029
(800) 422-4295
http://www.hawkhill.com

Insight Media
(Videos, CD-ROMs)
2162 Broadway, New York, NY 10024
(800) 233-9910
http://www.insight-media.com

JLM Visuals
(Videos, CD-ROMs, Slide Programs)
1208 Bridge Street, Grafton, WI 53024
(414) 377-7775
e-mail: JMLVisuals@aol.com

Teacher's Video Co.
(Videos)
Global Video, Inc., P.O. Box SCF-4455,
Scottsdale, AZ 85261
(800) 262-8837

Cell/Molecular Biology (CD-ROMs)	Multimedia Biology CyberEd. Inc., P.O. Box 3480, Chico, CA 95967-3480 (888) 318-0700 http://www.cyber-ed.com
Genetics, Evolution ***Statistics***	Exeter Sortware 47 Route 25A, Suite 2, East Setauket, NY 11733-2870 (800) 842-5892 e-mail: ExeterSftw@aol.com http://users.AOL.com/ExeterSftw
Genes and Gender (Videos)	Filmakers Library 124 E. 40th Street, New York, NY 10016 (212) 808-4980 e-mail:info@filmakers.com http://www.filmakers.com
NOVA Videos	WGBH Boston Video (800) 949-8670 FAX 802-864-9846 http://www.wgbh.org

Laboratory/Demonstration Instructional Kits

Carolina Biological	(800) 334-5551 http://www.carolina.com
Edvotek	P.O. Box 1232, West Bethesda, MD 20827-1232 (800) 338-6835 e-mail: edvotek@aol.com http://www.edvotek.com
Fisher Scientific	(800)766-7000 http://www.fishersci.com
Modern Biology, Inc.	111 North 500 West, West Lafayette, IN 47906 (800) 733-6544

http://www.modernbio.com

| VWR Scientific Products | (800) 727-4368 |
| | http://www.sargentwelch.com |

| Wards Biology | (800) 962-2660 |
| | http://www.wardsci.com |

Biotechnology

Modern Biology, Inc.	111 North 500 West, West Lafayette, IN 47906
	(800) 733-6544
	http://www.modernbio.com

Edvotek	P.O. Box 1232,
	West Bethesda, MD 20827-1232
	(800) 338-6835
	e-mail: edvotek@aol.com
	http://www.edvotek.com

WWW Resources for Helping Instructors and Students Locate Scientific Articles:

Student Guide to the Internet   Stull, A., and H. Nickla. 2000. *Science on the Internet: A Student's Guide* (2000-2001). Prentice Hall. Upper Saddle River, NJ 07458 http://www.prenhall.com

http://www.ncbi.nlm.nih.gov (National Library of Medicine, abstracts, full papers, through PubMed portion on menu. Many other useful applications available)

http://www.findarticles.com (Source of Articles from numerous areas including Primary Articles)

http://www.idealibrary.com (Access to Full Papers through IDEAL, your institution must subscribe to this service)

http://www.sciencedirect.com (Access to Full Papers through IDEAL, your institution must subscribe to this service)

http://www.biology.arizona.edu/default.html (The Biology Project, interactive, useful and interesting. Contains tutorials, animations, etc. on a variety of biology topics including genetics)

http://cgap.nci.nih.gov/ (The Cancer Genome Anatomy Project is an excellent resource for investigating genetic, chromosomal, metabolic, and anatomical aspects of cancer)

Careers in Genetics

Brendon, H. 1996. Going to Work in Genes Catches On. *Nature* 383:739
Gershon, D. 1996. Counseling Comes of Age. *Nature* 383:741

Internet Resources

Societies

A World of Genetics Societies (extremely useful for exploring sites related to genetics career information)
http://www.faseb.org/genetics/
http://www.faseb.org/genetics/careers2.htm

American Society of Human Genetics
http://www.faseb.org/genetics

The Genetics Society of Genetics
http://www.faseb.org/genetics/gsa/gsamenu.htm

American Board of Genetic Counseling
http://www.faseb.org/genetics/abgc/abgcmenu.htm

KUMC Human Genetics Careers
http://www.kumc.edu/gec/prof/career.html

National Society of Genetics Counselors
http://www.nsgc.org/

Human Genome Project - Genetic Counseling
http://www.ornl.gov/hgmis/medicine/genecounseling.html

Industry (examples)

Myriad Genetics
http://www.myriad.com/

Invitrogen
http://www.invitrogen.com/

Biology Careers

Science's Next Wave
http://www.nextwave.org

Chapter 1

Multiple Choice Format

1. The term *preformation* is most likely associated with which of the following?

    A.   Galen
    B.   homunculus
    C.   Mendel
    D.   pangenesis
    E.   hybridization

Answer: B

2. Joseph Gottlieb Kolreuter hybridized varieties of plants, observing both the variability of species and genetic segregation approximately 100 years before Gregor Mendel. Why is it felt that he did not recognize the significance of his work?

    A.   The microscope was not available to him.
    B.   Darwin's concepts of natural selection were opposed to his thinking.
    C.   He believed in special creation and the fixity of species.
    D.   There was too much opposition stemming from the observations of Gregor Mendel.
    E.   Lamarck suggested that the fixity of species was fact, and supportable by direct observation.

Answer: C

3. Much is known about early Greek thinking regarding heredity and variation. What two notable Greeks provided early speculations on the nature of human genetics?

    A.   Hippocrates and Aristotle
    B.   Darwin and Mendel
    C.   Lamarck and Kolreuter
    D.   Redi and Spalanzini
    E.   Pasteur and Galen

Answer: A

Sample Questions: Chapter 1 An Introduction to Genetics

4. The genetic material DNA or RNA consists of basic subunits called

      A.   mitochondria.
      B.   lysosomes.
      C.   centrioles.
      D.   nucleotides.
      E.   None of the above

Answer: D

5. List three immediate products of transcription that function in the production of the phenotype.

      A.   fats, carbohydrates, and nucleic acids
      B.   glycine, histidine, phenylalanine
      C.   nucleic acids, proteins, and amino acids
      D.   lipids, proteins, carbohydrates
      E.   rRNA, mRNA, tRNA

Answer: E

6. The branch of genetics that refers to the passage of genetic traits from one generation to the next is referred to as

      A.   eugenics.
      B.   euphenics.
      C.   transmission genetics.
      D.   recombinant DNA technology.
      E.   cytogenetics.

Answer: C

7. Genetics is the study of which of the following?

      A.   heredity and variation
      B.   mutation and recession
      C.   transcription and translation
      D.   diploid and haploid
      E.   replication and recombination

Answer: A

Sample Questions: Chapter 1 An Introduction to Genetics

Short Answer Format

8. Early in the twentieth century, several *cornerstones* of biology provided groundwork for the development of biology and eventually modern genetics. State at least two of these cornerstones.

Answer: cells are the fundamental units of life, cells contain nuclei which in turn contain chromosomes, chromosomes are constant in number within a species

9. Name two Greek philosophers who speculated on the nature of life and the generative forces that direct development of individual organisms. Both considered hypotheses to account for heredity and the roles of male and female gametes in the development of individual organisms.

Answer: Hippocrates, Aristotle

10. What is the name of a theory which states that organisms are derived from the assembly and reorganization, somewhat *de novo*, of substances in the egg?

Answer: epigenesis

11. In 1859, Charles Darwin published *The Origin of Species* in which he presented ideas on the causes of organismic change through time. A primary conceptual gap existed that left his theory open to criticism. What was that conceptual gap?

Answer: lack of understanding of the genetic basis of variation and inheritance

12. Name the individual who, working with the garden pea in the mid=1850s, demonstrated quantitative patterns of heredity and developed a theory involving the behavior of hereditary factors.

Answer: Gregor Mendel

13. What does the term *genetics* mean?

Answer: Genetics is a subdiscipline of biology concerned with the study of heredity and variation at the molecular, cellular, developmental, organismal, and populational levels.

14. Name the substance that serves as the hereditary material in eukaryotes and prokaryotes.

Answer: DNA or deoxyribonucleic acid is the hereditary material in eukaryotes and prokaryotes.

Sample Questions: Chapter 1 An Introduction to Genetics

15. Name two individuals who provided the conceptual basis for our present understanding of the origin of species.

Answer: Darwin, Wallace

16. The more classical investigative approach to genetics described patterns by which traits are passed through generations. What is the name of this approach?

Answer: transmission genetics

17. List two properties of DNA's nitrogenous bases that are necessary for DNA function.

Answer: hydrogen bonding and complementarity

18. Genetic engineering is not necessarily new. What activities have been occurring for centuries that have altered the genetic composition of nonhuman species?

Answer: domestication of animals and the cultivation of plants

19. Name three botanists who, in 1900, rediscovered the work of Gregor Mendel.

Answer: Correns, de Vries, Von Tschermak

20. Genetics is commonly seen as being grouped into several general areas: transmission, molecular, and population/evolution. What general activities are related to transmission genetics?

Answer: Mendelian inheritance (segregation and independent assortment), modification of Mendelian patterns, pedigree analysis, chromosome and karyotype analysis

21. What is meant by the term *eugenics*?

Answer: Eugenics, coined by Galton in 1883, refers to the direct application of genetic knowledge to influence the human condition.

Sample Questions: Chapter 1 An Introduction to Genetics

22. Distinguish between *positive* from *negative* eugenics.

Answer: Positive eugenics encourages parents with *favorable* traits to have offspring, while negative eugenics attempts to restrict reproduction of individuals with *undesired* characteristics.

23. To what activities might medical genetics refer?

Answer: genetic counseling, human genetic engineering, applications of biotechnology and genome sequencing

24. Name two human diseases that have been well characterized by geneticists.

Answer: sickle-cell anemia, erythroblastosis fetalis, cystic fibrosis, hemophilia, muscular dystrophy, Tay-Sachs disease, Down syndrome.

25. In Nazi Germany during the 1930s, one form of applied genetics based on scientifically invalid premises was extended to entire ethnic groups, Jews and gypsies. Name that form of applied genetics.

Answer: negative eugenics

26. What is meant by the term *euphenics*?

Answer: Euphenics refers to medical and/or genic intervention to reduce the impact of defective genotypes on individuals.

27. In nonviral systems, what is the nature of the hereditary substance?

Answer: DNA (deoxyribonucleic acid) is a double-stranded polymer organized as a double helix.

28. What is the goal of the Human Genome Project?

Answer: to accurately and completely sequence the 3.3 billion nucleotides constituting the human genome

Sample Questions: Chapter 1 An Introduction to Genetics

29. What is meant by the term *gene*?

Answer: A gene is a unit of heredity

30. Distinguish the functions of DNA and RNA in a eukaryote.

Answer: DNA is responsible for the storage and replication of genetic information, while RNA is involved in the expression of stored genetic information.

31. Name the bases in DNA and their hydrogen bonding specificities?

Answer: adenine:thymine, guanine:cytosine

32. What is meant be the term *epigenesis*?

Answer: Epigenesis refers to the fact that an organism is derived from substances in the egg, which differentiate during embryonic development. Body organs are not initially present in the early embryo.

33. Compare and contrast nonenzymatic and enzymatic proteins.

Answer: Both are gene products, with their primary structure being a string of amino acids. Enzymes are required as catalysts for most biochemical reactions, while nonenzymatic proteins include structural (collagen), protective (immunoglobins), and/or transport (hemoglobin) proteins.

34. List two relatively complex processes that are involved in the expression of genetic information.

Answer: transcription, translation

35. Describe two terms often used in the description of genetics.

Answer: Heredity, the similarity of parents and offspring and the similarity of members of the same species. Variation, the lack of similarity of parents and offspring and members of the same species.

Sample Questions: Chapter 1 An Introduction to Genetics

36. What is meant by the phrase "The Trinity of Molecular Genetics"?

Answer: functional and structural relationships among DNA, RNA, and protein

37. What is the composition of the genetic material?

Answer: polymers of nucleotides making up DNA

38. What is meant by *complementarity* in terms of molecular biology?

Answer: base pairing of AT or AU and GC

39. Reference is often made to adapter molecules when describing protein synthesis. What is being referred to by this term?

Answer: tRNA

40. Given that DNA is the genetic material in prokaryotes and eukaryotes, what other structures and substances are associated with expression of that genetic material?

Answer: RNA (messenger, ribosomal, transfer), ribosomes, enzymes, proteins

41. What is another term for a biological catalyst?

Answer: enzyme

42. List the names of individuals who played a role in the early development of ideas concerning heredity and variation.

Answer: Hippocrates, Aristotle, Lamarck, Linnaeus, Kolreuter, Darwin, Mendel, Correns, de Vries, Von Tschermak

43. The recent work involving the cloning of a sheep from a somatic cell was accomplished by Ian Wilmut at the Roslin Institute in Scotland. What was the name of the cloned sheep, and what was the purpose of generating this cloned organism?

Answer: The sheep's name was Dolly, and the purpose of the research was to use cloned mammals as models to study human disease and produce therapeutic drugs beneficial to humans.

Sample Questions: Chapter 1 An Introduction to Genetics

44. Provide a description of the study of population genetics.

Answer: Population genetics is the study of the origin and maintenance of genetic variation. Studies are usually related to the study of evolutionary processes and the prediction of gene frequencies in future generations.

45. English and American geneticists began distancing themselves from the eugenics movement even before the Nazi Party rose to power in the 1930s. Why?

Answer: Scientists were concerned about the scientific validity and evidence in support of eugenic premises.

True/False Format

46. Two early Greeks who speculated on the nature of heredity were Harvey and Aristotle.

Answer: False

47. Kolreuter provided insights into the nature of heredity through studies on plant hybridization.

Answer: True

48. Lamarck provided considerable insight into the evolutionary process by writing *The Origin of Species* in 1859.

Answer: False

49. Gregor Mendel's work was rediscovered in 1900 by three botanists named Correns, de Vries, and Von Tschermak.

Answer: True

50. Eugenics is so named because it is the true form of genetics, in contrast to euphenics, which is a false form of genetics.

Answer: False

51. Genetics is the study of heredity and variation.

Answer: True

Sample Questions: Chapter 1 An Introduction to Genetics

52. Complementarity in a genetic sense refers to the polymerization of nucleotides in DNA.

Answer: False

53. Transcription and translation are processes directly involved in gene expression.

Answer: True

54. The Human Genome Project seeks to determine the sequence of nucleotides in the human genome.

Answer: True

55. *Preformation* is a term correctly defining the process of epigenesis.

Answer: False

56. *Basic* research involves acquiring knowledge for its own sake, whereas *applied* research applies knowledge to solve problems facing society or to improve the wellbeing of members of society.

Answer: True

57. Involuntary sterilization of those considered less fit was never practiced in the United States.

Answer: False

58. At present, the two genetic modifications found in the majority of genetically modified crops are *Bt* pest resistance and glyphosate herbicide resistance.

Answer: True

59. Less than 5% of the soybeans and corn produced in the United States are grown from GM seeds and less than 10% of all processed foods in North America contain ingredients derived from GM plants.

Answer: False

60. There is worldwide acceptance of GM foods for human consumption.

Answer: False

Chapter 2

Multiple Choice Format

1. If a typical somatic cell has 32 chromosomes, how many chromosomes are expected in each gamete of that organism?

    A.   32
    B.   64
    C.   16
    D.   0
    E.   46

Answer: C

2. In an organism with 52 chromosomes, how many bivalents would be expected to form during meiosis? How many tetrads?

    A.   52
    B.   26
    C.   13
    D.   104
    E.   208

Answer: B

3. In a healthy male, how many sperm cells would be expected to be formed from (a) 400 primary spermatocytes? (b) 400 secondary spermatocytes?

    A.   (a) 800 (b) 800
    B.   (a) 1600 (b) 1600
    C.   (a) 1600 (b) 800
    D.   (a) 400 (b) 400
    E.   (a) 100 (b) 800

Answer: C

Sample Questions: Chapter 2   Mitosis and Meiosis

4. In a healthy female, how many secondary oocytes would be expected to form from 100 primary oocytes? How many first polar bodies?

    A.   200, 50
    B.   100, 50
    C.   200, 300
    D.   100, 100
    E.   50, 50

Answer: D

5. (a) Name two proteins known to be involved in the regulation of the mitotic cell cycle. (b) Name one protein that appears to serve as a significant tumor suppressor by triggering cell suicide in some cases.

    A.   (a) glycine, arginine (b) cdk
    B.   (a) hexokinase, cyclins (b) p53
    C.   (a) cyclin-dependent kinase, enzymes (b) hexokinase
    D.   (a) cyclin-dependent kinase, cyclins (b) p19
    E.   (a) cyclin-dependent kinase, cyclins (b) p53

Answer: E

6. What is the outcome of synapsis, a significant event in meiosis?

    A.   side by side alignment of nonhomologous chromosomes
    B.   dyad formation
    C.   monad movement to opposite poles
    D.   side-by-side alignment of homologous chromosomes
    E.   chiasma segregation

Answer: D

Sample Questions: Chapter 2   Mitosis and Meiosis

7. During interphase of the cell cycle,

      A.   DNA recombines.
      B.   sister chromatids move to opposite poles.
      C.   the nuclear membrane disappears.
      D.   RNA replicates.
      E.   DNA content essentially doubles.

Answer: E

Short Answer Format

8. The somatic cells of a particular male contain one pair of homologous chromosomes, e.g. R_1R_2, and one additional chromosome without a homologue, e.g., S. What chromosomal combinations would be expected in the meiotic products (spermatids) of a single primary spermatocyte? (There may be more than one answer.)

Answer: R_1S, R_1S, R_2, R_2 or R_1, R_1, R_2S, R_2S

9. Trisomy 21 or Down syndrome occurs when there is a normal diploid chromosomal complement of 46 chromosomes plus one (extra) chromosome #21. Such individuals therefore have 47 chromosomes.   Assume that a mating occurs between a female with Down syndrome and a normal 46-chromosome male. What proportion of the offspring would be expected to have Down syndrome? Justify your answer.

Answer: One half of the offspring will be expected to have Down syndrome because of 2 X 1 segregation of chromosome #21 at anaphase I.

10. Normal diploid somatic (body) cells of the mosquito *Culex pipiens* contain six chromosomes. Assign the symbols A^mA^p, B^mB^p, and C^mC^p to the three homologous chromosomal pairs. The "m" superscript indicates that the homologue is maternally derived, while the "p" indicates a paternally derived homologue. Assume that in the genus *Culex,* the sex chromosomes are morphologically identical.

    (a) For each of the cell types given below, draw and label (with reference to the symbols defined above) an expected chromosomal configuration.

    Mitotic metaphase
    Metaphase of meiosis I
    Metaphase of meiosis II

(b) The stage at which "sister chromatids go to opposite poles" immediately follows which of the above stages?

(c) Assuming that all nuclear DNA is restricted to chromosomes and that the amount of nuclear DNA essentially doubles during the S phase of interphase, how much nuclear DNA would be present in each cell listed above? Note: Assume that the G1 nucleus of a mosquito cell contains 3.0×10^{-12} grams of DNA.

(d) Given that the sexes of *Culex* are determined by alleles of one gene, males heterozygous, *Mm*, and females homozygous, *mm*, illustrate a labeled chromosomal configuration (involving the symbols A^mA^p, B^mB^p, and C^mC^p and the *M* locus) in a primary spermatocyte at metaphase. Assume that the *M* locus is on the A^mA^p chromosome and that crossing over has not occurred between the *M* locus and the centromere.

Answer:
(a)

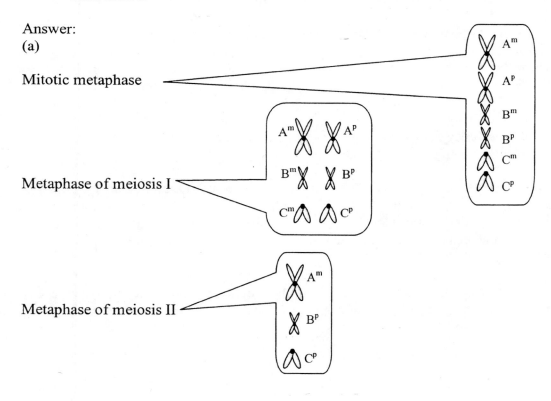

(b) metaphase of meiosis II

(c) 6, 6, 3

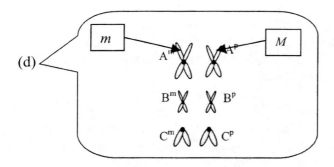

(d)

11. *Drosophila melanogaster,* the fruit fly, has a 2*n* chromosome number of 8. Assume that you are microscopically examining mitotic and meiotic cells of this organism. You note that in the female, two chromosomal pairs are metacentric, two pairs are acrocentric.

(a) Draw the chromosomal configurations as you would expect to see them at the stages listed:

Mitotic metaphase	First polar body (metaphase)
Primary oocyte (metaphase)	Ootid (G1)
Secondary oocyte (metaphase)	

(b) Given that the above-mentioned cells are from individuals heterozygous for two independently segregating, autosomal loci, *plum eyes* and *curled wings*, place appropriate symbols (of your designation) on chromosomes in the drawings you made in part (a) above. Assume no crossing over, and there may be more than one correct answer in some cases.

(c) Assuming that a somatic G2 nucleus from the individuals mentioned above contains about 8.0 picograms of DNA, how much nuclear DNA would you expect in each of the cells mentioned above?

Sample Questions: Chapter 2   Mitosis and Meiosis

Answer:

(a, b)

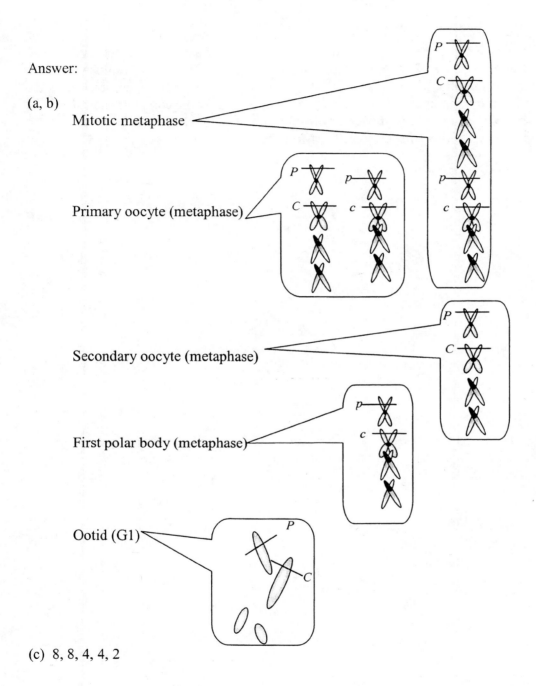

Mitotic metaphase

Primary oocyte (metaphase)

Secondary oocyte (metaphase)

First polar body (metaphase)

Ootid (G1)

(c) 8, 8, 4, 4, 2

Sample Questions: Chapter 2 Mitosis and Meiosis

12. Down syndrome, or trisomy 21, in humans is caused by an extra copy of the relatively small, acrocentric chromosome #21. With respect to chromosome #21, the X chromosome (medium in size and somewhat metacentric) and the Y chromosome (small and acrocentric) draw a possible array of chromosomes in the four sperm cells produced by the complete meiosis of one primary spermatocyte. For the purposes of this question, assume that males with Down syndrome produce normal ratios of sperm cells. (More than one answer is possible.)

Answer:

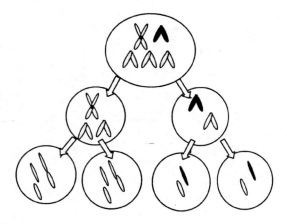

13. Assume that an organism has a diploid chromosome number of 6. Two chromosomal pairs are telocentric, the other pair is metacentric. Assume that the sex chromosomes are morphologically identical. Draw chromosomes as you would expect them to appear at the following stages:

      Primary oocyte (metaphase)
      Secondary spermatocyte (metaphase)
      First polar body (metaphase)

Sample Questions: Chapter 2   Mitosis and Meiosis

Answer:

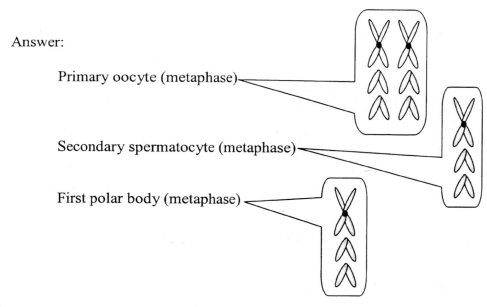

Primary oocyte (metaphase)

Secondary spermatocyte (metaphase)

First polar body (metaphase)

14. Assume that you are examining a cell under a microscope and you observe the following as the total chromosomal constituents of a nucleus. You know that $2n = 2$ in this organism, that all chromosomes are metacentric, and that each G1 cell nucleus contains 8 picograms of DNA.

(a) Circle the correct stage for this cell:
   anaphase of mitosis
   anaphase of meiosis I
   anaphase of meiosis II
   telophase of mitosis

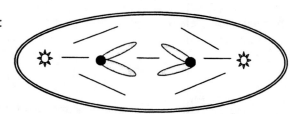

(b) How many picograms of chromosomal DNA would you expect in the cell shown above?

Answer:

(a) anaphase of meiosis II
(b) 8

Sample Questions: Chapter 2   Mitosis and Meiosis

15. There is about as much nuclear DNA in a primary spermatocyte as in _____ (how many) spermatids?

Answer: 4

16. You may have heard through various media of an animal alleged to be the hybrid of a rabbit and a cat. Given that the cat (*Felis domesticus*) has a diploid chromosome number of 38 and a rabbit (*Oryctolagus cuniculus*) has a diploid chromosome number of 44, what would be the expected chromosome number in the somatic tissues of this alleged hybrid?

Answer: 41

17. The horse *Equus caballus* has 32 pairs of chromosomes, while the donkey (*Equus asinus*) has 31 pairs of chromosomes. How many chromosomes would be expected in the somatic tissue of mule hybrid?

Answer: 63

18. Name two evolutionarily significant benefits of meiosis that are not present in mitosis.

Answer: reshuffling of homologous chromosomes and crossing over

19. How many haploid sets of chromosomes are present in an individual cell with a chromosome number of 46? 32?

Answer: 2, 2

20. How many haploid sets of chromosomes are present in an individual cell that is tetraploid (4n)?

Answer: 4

21. The nucleolus organizer (NOR) is responsible for producing what type of cell structure?

Answer: ribosome

22. Regarding the mitotic cell cycle, what is meant by a *checkpoint*?

Answer: A checkpoint is a portion of a cell cycle that is sensitive to a variety of conditions influencing the eventual health of the cell or individual. Such checkpoints often restrict passage to the next event in the cell cycle.

Sample Questions: Chapter 2 Mitosis and Meiosis

23. What is meant by the term *chiasma*?

Answer: A chiasma is an area where chromatids intertwine during meiosis.

24. List four terms used to describe the morphology, with respect to arm ratio, of eukaryotic chromosomes.

Answer: metacentric, submetacentric, acrocentric, telocentric

25. Name two cellular organelles, each having genetic material, that are involved in either photosynthesis or respiration.

Answer: chloroplasts and mitochondria

26. Homologous chromosomes are those that can be matched by virtue of their similar structure and function within a nucleus. What chromosomes making up a genome do not follow the same characteristics of homology?

Answer: sex-determining chromosomes

27. After what meiotic stage would one expect monads to be formed?

Answer: meiosis II

28. List, in order of appearance, the cell types expected to be formed during (a) spermatogenesis and (b) oogenesis.

Answer: (a) spermatogonia, primary spermatocyte, secondary spermatocyte, spermatid, spermatozoa; (b) oogonium, primary oocyte, secondary oocyte and first polar body, ootid and second polar body

29. List, in order of occurrence, the phases of (a) mitosis and (b) prophase I of meiosis.

Answer: (a) prophase, prometaphase, metaphase, anaphase, telophase; (b) leptonema, zygonema, pachynema, diplonema, diakinesis

30. Two terms, *reductional* and *equational*, generally refer to which stages of meiosis?

Answer: meiosis I and meiosis II, respectively

Sample Questions: Chapter 2   Mitosis and Meiosis

31. Between which stages of mitosis is GO located?

Answer: G1 and S

32. In human oogenesis, when does (a) the first meiotic division occur, and (b) the second meiotic division occur?

Answer: (a) ovulation, (b) fertilization

33. During interphase, only dispersed _____ fibers are present in the nucleus.

Answer: chromatin

34. Scrutiny at the G1/S checkpoint is dependent on a protein called _____. This protein functions in the progression of _____, programmed cell death.

Answer: p53, apoptosis

35. A particular cell cycle checkpoint assesses the successful formation of the spindle fiber system and the attachment of the spindle fibers to the kinetochores. This checkpoint is call the

_____.

Answer: M checkpoint

36. When cells withdraw from the continuous cell cycle and enter a "resting" phase, they are said to be in _____.

Answer: G0

37. The house fly, *Musca domestica*, has a haploid chromosome number of 6. How many chromatids should be present in a diploid, somatic, metaphase cell?

Answer: 24

True/False Format

38. A chromosome may contain one or two chromatids in different phases of the mitotic or meiotic cell cycle.

Answer: True

Sample Questions: Chapter 2   Mitosis and Meiosis

39. A gamete is haploid (n) and contains 1 C DNA.

Answer: True

40. A prophase I cell is $2n$ and contains 4 C DNA.

Answer: True

41. During meiosis, chromosome number reduction takes place in anaphase II.

Answer: False

42. Assuming Mendelian laws apply, if the genotype of the parents is known, the genotypic ratio of the offspring can be predicted (calculated) with certainty.

Answer: True

43. If the genotype of the parents is known, the phenotypic ratio of the offspring can be predicted (calculated) with certainty.

Answer: False

44. If two homozygous deaf persons have children with normal hearing, the mutations causing deafness are in the same gene.

Answer: False

45. S phase is the part of interphase when DNA duplication takes place.

Answer: True

46. The centromere of a chromosome separates during anaphase.

Answer: True

47. A bivalent at pachytene contains four chromatids.

Answer: True

48. The meiotic cell cycle involves two cell divisions but only one DNA replication.

Answer: True

Chapter 3

Multiple Choice Format

1. Name at least three scientists who, around the year 1900, were influential in setting the stage for our present understanding of transmission genetics.

       A.   Beadle, Tatum, Lederberg
       B.   Watson, Crick, Wilkins, Franklin
       C.   DeVries, Correns, Tschermak, Sutton, Boveri
       D.   Darwin, Mendel, Lamarck
       E.   Hippocrates, Aristotle, Kolreuter

Answer: C

2. Name the single individual whose work in the mid-nineteenth century contributed to our understanding of the particulate nature of inheritance as well as basic genetic transmission patterns. With what organism did this person work?

       A.   Gregor Mendel, *Pisum sativum* (pea)
       B.   George Beadle, *Neurospora* (fungus)
       C.   Thomas Hunt Morgan, *Drosophila* (fruit fly)
       D.   Calvin Bridges, *Drosophila* (fruit fly)
       E.   Boris Ephrussi, *Ephestia* (moth)

Answer: A

3. An allele is

       A.   one of the bases in DNA.
       B.   an alternate form of a gene.
       C.   another term for epistasis.
       D.   present only in males and is responsible for sex determination.
       E.   found in mitochondria but not in nuclei.

Answer: B

Sample Questions: Chapter 3   Mendelian Genetics

4. What types of ratios are likely to occur in crosses when dealing with a single gene pair?

    A.   9:3:3:1, 1:2:1
    B.   1:1:1:1, 1:4:6:4:1
    C.   3:1, 1:1, 1:2:1
    D.   9:7, 12:3:1
    E.   15:1, 1:2

Answer: C

5. Apply the product law to a coin-flip situation. What is the probability that on three flips of a coin, heads will occur on all three flips?

    A.   1/4
    B.   1/2
    C.   3/16
    D.   1/8
    E.   Insufficient information to answer this question.

Answer: D

6. The fundamental Mendelian process involving the separation of contrasting genetic elements at the same locus is called

    A. segregation.
    B. independent assortment.
    C. continuous variation.
    D. discontinuous variation.
    E. dominance or recessiveness.

Answer: A

7. The chi-square test involves statistical comparison between measured (observed) and predicted (expected) values. One generally determines degrees of freedom as

    A. the number of categories being compared.
    B. one less than the number of classes being compared.
    C. one more than the number of classes being compared.
    D. ten minus the sum of the two categories.
    E.   the sum of the two categories.

Answer: B

Sample Questions: Chapter 3   Mendelian Genetics

Short Answer Format

8. Assume that in a series of experiments, plants with round seeds were crossed to plants with wrinkled seeds and the following offspring were obtained: 220 round; 180 wrinkled.

(a)   What is the most probable genotype of each parent?
(b)   What genotypic and phenotypic ratios are expected?
(c)   Based on the information provided in part (b) above, what are the expected (theoretical) numbers of progeny of each phenotypic class?

Answer:

(a) Assuming that round (W) is dominant to wrinkled (w): Ww X ww
(b) 1:1
(c) 200

9. Gray seed color in peas is dominant to white. Assume that Mendel conducted a series of experiments where plants with gray seeds were crossed among themselves and the following progeny were produced: 320 gray and 80 white. (a) What is the most probable genotype of each parent? (b) Based on your answer in part (a) above, what genotypic and phenotypic ratios are expected in the progeny?

Answer:

(a) Assuming the following symbols: G = gray and g = white, Gg X Gg
(b) genotypic = 1:2:1, phenotypic = 3:1

10. Assume you have a garden, and some pea plants have solid leaves and others have striped leaves. You conduct a series of crosses and obtain the results given in the table.

Cross		Progeny	
		Solid	*Striped*
(a)	solid X striped	55	60
(b)	solid X solid	36	0
(c)	striped X striped	0	65
(d)	solid X solid	92	30
(e)	solid X striped	44	0

Define gene symbols and give the possible genotypes of the parents of each cross.

Answer:

Sample Questions: *Chapter 3   Mendelian Genetics*

(a) From cross (d), assume that solid (*S*) is dominant to striped (*s*): *Ss* X *ss*

(b) *SS* X *SS* or *SS* X *Ss*

(c) *ss* X *ss*

(d) *Ss* X *Ss*

(e) *SS* X *ss*

11.   In *Drosophila melanogaster*, vestigial (short) wings (*vg*) are caused by a recessive gene that independently assorts with a gene pair that influences body hair. Hairy (*h*) results in a hairy body. A cross is made between a fly with normal wings and a hairy body and a fly with vestigial wings and a normal body. The phenotypically normal F1 flies were crossed among each other and 1024 F2 flies were reared. What phenotypes would you expect in the F2, and in what actual numbers (not ratio) would you expect to find them?

Answer:

Phenotypes: wild, vestigial, hairy, vestigial hairy

Numbers expected: wild (576), vestigial (192), hairy (192), vestigial hairy (64)

12.   Two organisms, *AABBCCDDEE* and *aabbccddee*, are mated to produce an F1, which is self-fertilized. If the capital letters represent dominant, independently assorting alleles,

(a)   how many different genotypes will occur in the F2?

(b)   what proportion of the F2 genotypes will be recessive for all five loci?

(c)   would you change your answers (a and/or b) if the initial cross occurred between
          AAbbCCddee X *aaBBccDDEE* parents?

(d)   would you change your answers (a and/or b) if the initial cross occurred between
          AABBCCDDEE X *aabbccddEE* parents?

Answer:

(a) $3^5 = 243$

(b) 1/243

(c) no

(d) yes

13. How many different kinds of gametes can be produced by an individual with the genotype *AABbCCddEeFf*?

Answer: $2^3 = 8$

Sample Questions: Chapter 3   Mendelian Genetics

14. Albinism, a lack of pigmentation in humans, results from an autosomal recessive gene (a). Two parents with normal pigmentation have an albino child.

(a) What is the probability that their next child will be albino?
(b) What is the probability that their next child will be an albino girl?
(c) What is the probability that their next three children will be albino?

Answer:

(a) 1/4
(b) 1/4 X 1/2 = 1/8
(c) 1/4 X 1/4 X 1/4 = 1/6

15. *Dentinogenesis imperfecta* is a rare, autosomal, dominantly inherited disease of the teeth that occurs about one in 8000. The teeth are somewhat brown in color, and the crowns wear down rapidly. Assume that a male with *dentinogenesis imperfecta* and no family history of the disease marries a woman with normal teeth. What is the probability that

(a) their first child will have *dentinogenesis imperfecta*?
(b) their first two children will have *dentinogenesis imperfecta*?
(c) their first child will be a girl with *dentinogenesis imperfecta*?

Answer:

(a)   1/2
(b)   1/2 X 1/2 = 1/4
(c)   1/2 X 1/2 = 1/4

16. A certain type of congenital deafness in humans is caused by a rare autosomal dominant gene.

(a) In a mating involving a deaf man and a deaf woman (both heterozygous), would you expect all the children to be deaf? Explain your answer.

(b) In a mating involving a deaf man and a deaf women (both heterozygous), could all the children have normal hearing? Explain your answer.

(c) Another form of deafness is caused by a rare autosomal recessive gene. In a mating involving a deaf man and a deaf woman, could some of the children have normal hearing? Explain your answer.

Sample Questions: Chapter 3   Mendelian Genetics

Answer:

(a) No. In a mating involving heterozygotes, three genotypic classes are expected in the offspring: fully dominant, fully recessive, and heterozygous.

(b) Assuming that the parents are heterozygotes (because the gene is rare), it is possible that all of the children could have normal hearing.

(c) Since the gene in question is recessive, both of the parents are homozygous and one would not expect normal hearing in the offspring.

17. Among dogs, short hair is dominant to long hair and dark coat color is dominant to white (albino) coat color. Assume that these two coat color traits are caused by independently segregating gene pairs. For each of the crosses given below, write the most probable genotype (or genotypes, if more than one answer is possible) for the parents. It is important that you select a realistic symbol set and define each symbol below:

Parental Phenotypes   *Phenotypes of Offspring*

		Short Dark	Long Dark	Short Albino	Long Albino
(a)	dark, short X dark, long	26	24	0	0
(b)	albino, short X albino, short	0	0	102	33
(c)	dark, short X albino, short	16	0	16	0
(d)	dark, short X dark, short	175	67	61	21

Assume that for cross (d) above you were interested in determining whether fur color follows a 3:1 ratio. Set up, but don't complete the calculations, a chi-square test for these data (fur color in cross (d)).

Answer:

Let A = dark, a = albino and L = short and l = long

(a)   *AALl* X *AAll*   or *AALl* X *Aall*
(b)   *aaLl* X *aaLl*
(c)   *AaLL* X *aaLL* or *AaLl* X *aaLL*   or *AaLL* X *aaLl*
(d)   *AaLl* X *AaLl*

$$\chi^2 = \Sigma \frac{(o-e)^2}{e} = \frac{(242 - 243)^2}{243} + \frac{(82 - 81)^2}{81}$$

Sample Questions: Chapter 3 Mendelian Genetics

18. What types of ratios are likely to occur in crosses when dealing with two completely dominant, independently segregating gene pairs?

Answer: 9:3:3:1, 1:1:1:1

19. Provide a simple definition for *segregation* and *independent assortment*.

Answer: Segregation is the separation of alleles during meiosis, while independent assortment states that a member of one gene pair has an equal and independent opportunity of segregating with either member of another gene pair.

20. In what ways is sample size related to statistical testing?

Answer: By increasing sample size, one increases the reliability of the statistical test and decreases the likelihood of erroneous conclusions from chance fluctuations in the data

21. In a chi-square analysis, when does one reject (fail to accept) the null hypothesis?

Answer: usually when the probability value is less than 0.05

22. If one is testing a *goodness of fit* to a 9:3:3:1 ratio, how many degrees of freedom would be associated with the chi-square analysis?

Answer: number of classes minus 1 = 3

23. Assuming no crossing over between the gene in question and the centromere, when do alleles segregate during meiosis?

Answer: meiosis I, when homologous chromosomes go to opposite poles

24. Assuming a typical monohybrid cross in which one allele is completely dominant to the other, what ratio is expected if the F1s are crossed?

Answer: 3:1

25. Under what conditions does one expect a 9:3:3:1 ratio?

Answer: dihybrid cross (F2) with independently assorting, completely dominant genes

26. Under what conditions does one expect a 1:1:1:1 ratio?

Answer: A cross involving doubly heterozygous individuals crossed to fully recessive individuals. Genes involved assort independently of each other.

Sample Questions: Chapter 3   Mendelian Genetics

27. What is the probability of flipping a penny and a nickel and obtaining one head and one tail?

Answer: 1/2 (apply the sum law)

28. How many different kinds of gametes will be expected by an individual with the following genotype *PpCcTTRr*?

Answer: 8

29. Assume that a chi-square test was conducted to test the goodness of fit to a 9:3:3:1 ratio and a chi-square value of 10.62 was obtained. Should the null hypothesis be accepted?

Answer: No

30. Assume that a chi-square test was conducted to test the goodness of fit to a 3:1 ratio and a chi-square value of 2.62 was obtained. Should the null hypothesis be accepted? How many degrees of freedom would be associated with this test of significance?

Answer: Yes, 1

31. Assume that a Chi-square test provided a probability value of 0.02. Should the null hypothesis be accepted?

Answer: No

32. In studies of human genetics, usually a single individual brings the condition to the attention of a scientist or physician. When pedigrees are developed to illustrate transmission of the trait, what term does one use to refer to this individual?

Answer: proband

33. Albinism, lack of pigmentation in man, results from an autosomal recessive gene (*a*). Two parents with normal pigmentation have an albino child. What is the probability that their next child will be albino?

Answer: 1/4

34. Albinism, a lack of pigmentation in humans, results from an autosomal recessive gene (*a*). Two parents with normal pigmentation have an albino child. What is the probability that their next child will be an albino girl?

Answer: 1/4 X 1/2 = 1/8

Sample Questions: Chapter 3   Mendelian Genetics

35. Albinism, a lack of pigmentation in humans, results from an autosomal recessive gene (*a*). Two parents with normal pigmentation have an albino child. What is the probability that their next three children will be albino?

Answer: 1/4   X   1/4   X   1/4   =   1/64

36. The autosomal gene for brachydactyly, short fingers, is dominant to normal finger length. Assume that a female with brachydactyly in the heterozygous condition is married to a man with normal fingers. What is the probability that

(a) their first child will have brachydactyly?
(b) their first two children will have brachydactyly?
(c) their first child will be a brachydactylous girl?

Answers:

(a)   1/2
(b)   1/2   X   1/2   =   1/4
(c)   1/2   X   1/2   =   1/4

37. Tightly curled hair is caused by a dominant autosomal gene in humans. This trait is rare among northern Europeans.   If a curly-haired northern European marries a person with straight hair, what phenotypes (and in what proportions) are expected in the offspring?

Answer: 1/2 curly (because the curly-haired individual in most likely heterozygous), 1/2 straight hair

38. A certain type of congenital deafness in humans is caused by a rare autosomal dominant gene. In a mating involving a deaf man and a deaf woman (both heterozygous), would you expect all the children to be deaf? Explain your answer.

Answer: No. In a mating involving heterozygotes, three genotypic classes are expected in the offspring: fully dominant, fully recessive, and heterozygous.

39. A certain type of congenital deafness in humans is caused by a rare autosomal dominant gene. In a mating involving a deaf man and a deaf woman, could all the children have normal hearing? Explain your answer.

Answer: Assuming that the parents are heterozygotes (because the gene is rare), it is possible that all of the children could have normal hearing.

Sample Questions: Chapter 3 Mendelian Genetics

40. A certain type of congenital deafness in humans is caused by a rare autosomal recessive gene. In a mating involving a deaf man and a deaf woman, could some of the children have normal hearing? Explain your answer.

Answer: Since the gene in question is recessive, both of the parents are homozygous and one would not expect normal hearing in the offspring.

41. For the purposes of this question, assume that being Rh^+ is a consequence of D, and Rh^- individuals are *dd*. The ability to taste phenylthiocarbamide (PTC) is determined by the gene symbolized T (*tt* are nontasters). A female whose mother was Rh^- has the MN blood group, is Rh^+ and a nontaster of PTC and is married to a man who is MM, Rh^-, and a nontaster. List the possible genotypes of the children. Assume that all the loci discussed in this problem are autosomal and independently assorting.

Answer: *MMDdtt, MMddtt, MNDdtt, MNddtt*

42. What conditions are likely to apply if the progeny from the cross *AaBb* X *AaBb* appear in the 9:3:3:1 ratio?

Answer: complete dominance, independent assortment, no gene interaction

43. Assume that a cross is made between a heterozygous tall pea plant and a homozygous short pea plant. Fifty offspring are produced in the following frequency:

  30 = tall
  20 = short

(a) What frequency of tall and short plants is expected?

(b) If one wanted to test the *goodness of fit* between the observed and expected values, provide a statement of the null hypothesis.

(c) Compute a chi-square value associated with the appropriate test of significance.

(d) How many degrees of freedom are associated with this test of significance?

Answers:

(a) 1:1 (25 tall and 25 short)
(b) The deviations from a 1:1 ratio (25 tall and 25 short) are due to chance.
(c) $\chi^2 = 2$
(d) 1

Sample Questions: Chapter 3 Mendelian Genetics

44. According to the postulate of _____, all possible combinations of gametes will be formed in equal frequency.

Answer: independent assortment

45. Assuming independent assortment, what proportion of the offspring of the cross *AaBbCcDd* X *AabbCCdd* will have the *aabbccdd* genotype?

Answer: zero

46. In a statistical sense, as the sample size increases, the average deviation from the expected fraction or ratio is expected to _____.

Answer: decrease

47. In a chi-square test, as the value of the χ^2 increases, the likelihood of rejecting the null hypothesis _____.

Answer: increases

48. The individual whose phenotype drew the scientist to the family is called the _____.

Answer: propositus if male, proposita if female

49. What is the probability that the first two children of a couple will be male?

Answer: ½ X ½ = ¼ (product law)

50. What is the probability that the first two children of a couple will be of opposite sex?

Answer: ½ = male X ½ = female = ¼   *or* ½ = female X ½ = male = ¼

therefore: (sum law) ¼ + ¼ = ½

51. Albinism is a rare autosomal recessive disorder in humans. John has a sister who is albino and he marries Susan who has a brother with albinism. No other relatives are albino and there is no other family history of albinism. What is the probability that the first child of John and Susan will be normal (not albino)?

Answer: 2/3 X 2/3 X 1/4 = 1/9 for albinism and for normal, 8/9

True/False Format

Sample Questions: Chapter 3 Mendelian Genetics

52. Mendel's Law of Independent Assortment is supported by a 1:1:1:1 testcross ratio.

Answer: True

53. Mendel's Law of Segregation is supported by a 1 : 1 testcross ratio.

Answer: True

54. Mendel's discoveries were well received and understood by his contemporaries.

Answer: False

55. The nonfunctional form of a gene is called a wildtype allele.

Answer: False

56. A gene can have a maximum of two alleles.

Answer: False

57. To test Mendel's Law of Segregation, the experimenter needs a minimum of two contrasting forms of a gene.

Answer: True

58. To test Mendel's Law of Independent Assortment, the experimenter needs a minimum of two different genes and their two alleles.

Answer: True

59. A 1:1 phenotypic ratio is expected from a monohybrid testcross with complete dominance.

Answer: True

60. Assuming complete dominance, a 3:1 phenotypic ratio is expected from a monohybrid or self-cross.

Answer: True

61. A 9:3:3:1 phenotypic ratio is expected from a dihybrid testcross.

Answer: False

Sample Questions: Chapter 4   Modification of Mendelian Ratios

Chapter 4

Multiple Choice Format

1. With incomplete dominance, a likely ratio resulting from a monohybrid cross would be

  A. 3:3.
  B. 1:2:2:4.
  C. 1:2:1.
  D. 9:3:3:1.
  E. 3:1.

Answer: C

2. A situation where there are multiple alternative forms of a given gene is called

  A. multiple alleles.
  B. alternation of generations.
  C. codominance.
  D. incomplete dominance.
  E. hemizygosity.

Answer: A

3. A condition in which one gene pair masks the expression of a non-allelic gene pair is called

  A. codominance.
  B. epistasis.
  C. dominance.
  D. recessiveness.
  E. additive alleles.

Answer: B

Sample Questions: *Chapter 4 Modification of Mendelian Ratios*

4. Typical ratios resulting from epistatic interactions in dihybrid crosses would be

      A.   9:3:3:1, 1:2:1.
      B.   1:1:1:1, 1:4:6:4:1.
      C.   9:3:4, 9:7.
      D.   1:2:2:4:1:2:1:2:1.
      E.   3:1, 1:1.

Answer: C

5. Hemizygosity would most likely be associated with which of the following?

      A.   codominance
      B.   incomplete dominance
      C.   trihybrid crosses
      D.   sex-linked inheritance
      E.   sex-limited inheritance

Answer: D

6. A human condition that results from an interaction between Rh blood group alleles is known as

      A. allelism.
      B. the Bombay phenotype.
      C. isoagglutinogen.
      D. multiple allelism.
      E. erythroblastosis fetalis.

Answer: E

7. Because of the mechanism of sex determination, males of many species can be neither homozygous or heterozygous. Such males are said to be

      A. dominant.
      B. hemizygous.
      C. recessive.
      D. complementary.
      E. None of the above .

Answer: B

Sample Questions: Chapter 4   Modification of Mendelian Ratios

8. Forms of inheritance that do not follow typical Mendelian patterns and that appear to be more influenced by the parent contributing the most cytoplasm to the embryo are grouped under the general heading of

    A.   sex-linked inheritance.
    B.   neo-Mendelian inheritance.
    C.   extrachromosomal inheritance.
    D.   suppressive inheritance.
    E.   dominance and/or recessiveness.

Answer: C

9. Which of the following organelles are involved in the general category of organelle heredity?

    A.   mitochondria and chloroplasts
    B.   R factors
    C.   lysosomes and peroxisomes
    D.   F factors and episomes
    E.   Golgi and rough endoplasmic reticulum

Answer: A

10. Direction of shell coiling in the snail *Limnaea peregra* is conditioned by a form of extrachromosomal inheritance known as

    A.   sex-linked inheritance.
    B.   heteroplasmy.
    C.   maternal effect.
    D.   independent assortment.
    E.   epistasis.

Answer: C

Sample Questions: Chapter 4 Modification of Mendelian Ratios

11. The maternal effect in *Limnaea* is such that the genotype of the egg determines the direction of shell coiling regardles of the genotype of the offspring. Apparently the cause of this spectacular maternal effect results from

     A.   orientation of the spindle apparatus in early cleavage.
     B.   genophores present in the egg cytoplasm.
     C.   the F factor exerting its influence on the centrosome.
     D.   colicins "poisoning" one of the cleavage centers.
     E.   allelic substitution as demonstrated by RNA injection experiments.

Answer: A

12. One explanation for organelle inheritance is that

     A.   mitochondria and chloroplasts lack DNA and are therefore dependent on the maternal cytoplasmic contributions.
     B.   mitochondria and chloroplasts have DNA, which is subject to mutation.
     C.   organelles such as mitochondria are always wildtype.
     D.   chloroplasts, for example, are completely dependent on the nuclear genome for components.
     E.   None of the above

Answer: B

Short Answer Format

13. Assume that a dihybrid cross (*AaBb* X *AaBb*) is made in which the gene loci are autosomal, independently assorting, and incompletely dominant. What phenotypic ratio would you expect from such a cross? Just provide the ratio, not the phenotypes.

Answer: 1:2:1:2:4:2:1:2:1

14. Many of the color varieties of summer squash are determined by several interacting loci: *AA* or *Aa* give white, *aaBB* or *aaBb* give yellow, and *aabb* produces green. Assume that two fully heterozygous plants are crossed. Give the phenotypes (with frequencies) of the offspring.

Answer: 12 (white) : 3 (yellow): 1(green)

Sample Questions: Chapter 4   Modification of Mendelian Ratios

15. In mice, there is a set of multiple alleles of a gene for coat color. Four of those alleles are listed below.

$$C \quad = \text{full color (wild)},$$
$$c^{ch} = \text{chinchilla},$$
$$c^{d} \quad = \text{dilution},$$
$$c \quad = \text{albino}$$

Given that the gene locus is not sex-linked and that each allele is dominant to those lower in the list, diagram the crosses indicated below, and give the phenotypic ratios expected from each.

(a) wild (heterozygous for dilution) X chinchilla (heterozygous for albino)
(b) chinchilla (heterozygous for albino) X albino

Answer:

(a) Cc^{d} X $c^{ch}c$ $\Longrightarrow$ 2 full color: 1 chinchilla: 1 dilution
(b) $c^{ch}c$ X cc $\Longrightarrow$ 1 chinchilla: 1 albino

16. A mutant gene that produces brown eyes (*bw*) is located on chromosome #2 of *Drosophila melanogaster* whereas a mutant gene producing bright red eyes, scarlet (*st*), is located on chromosome #3. Phenotypically wildtype flies (with dull red eyes) whose mothers had brown eyes and whose fathers had scarlet eyes were mated. The 800 offspring possessed the following phenotypes: wildtype (dull red), white, scarlet (bright red), and brown. Most of the 800 offspring had wildtype eyes, while those with white eyes were the least frequent.

(a) Using standard symbolism, diagram the cross from the P generation (brown-eyed mothers X scarlet-eyed fathers) and the F1 generation. Be certain to provide the alleles of the mutant genes.

(b) From the information presented above, how many white-eyed flies would you expect in the F2 generation?

Answer:

(a)   P: $bw/bw; st^{+}/st^{+}$ X $bw^{+}/bw^{+}; st/st$

F1: $bw^{+}/bw; st^{+}/st$ X $bw^{+}/bw; st^{+}/st$

(b)   50

Sample Questions: Chapter 4   Modification of Mendelian Ratios

17.   In the mouse, gene *A* allows pigmentation to be deposited in the individual coat hairs, while its allele *a*   prevents such deposition of pigment. Gene *B* gives agouti (wildtype fur), while its allele *b* gives black fur.

(a) Diagram the cross between a doubly heterozygous agouti mouse mated with a fully homozygous recessive white mouse.

(b) What would be the expected phenotypic ratio in the progeny?

Answer:

(a)   *AaBb* X   *aabb*

(b)   1 (agouti): 1 (black): 2 (albino)

18. The trait of medium-sized leaves in iris is determined by the genetic condition *PP'*. Plants with large leaves are *PP,* while plants with small leaves are *P'P'*. A cross is made between two plants each with medium-sized leaves. If they produce 80 seedlings, what phenotypes and in what numbers would you expect?

Answer: 20 (large leaves), 40 (medium leaves), 20 (small leaves)

19. The trait for medium-sized leaves in iris is determined by the genetic condition *PP'*. Plants with large leaves are *PP* while plants with small leaves are *P'P'*. The trait for red flowers is controlled by the genes *RR*, pink by *RR',* and white by *R'R'*. A cross is made between two plants, each with medium-sized leaves and pink flowers.   If they produce 320 seedlings, what phenotypes and in what numbers would you expect? Assume no linkage.

Answer: 20 large, red
              40 medium, red
              20 small, red
              40 large, pink
              80 medium, pink
              40 small, pink
              20 large, white
              40 medium, white
              20 small, white

Sample Questions: Chapter 4 Modification of Mendelian Ratios

20. What is meant by the term *epistasis*? Distinguish between *epistasis* and *dominance*. Do not use examples in answering this question.

Answer: Epistasis refers to cases where a gene (or genes) of one pair masks the expression of a gene (or genes) at a different locus. Dominance refers to the form of expression of a gene in relation to its allele (or alleles). When a gene is dominant, the heterozygous combination is the same phenotypically as one of the homozygotes. Epistasis is a nonallelic interaction, while dominance is an allelic interaction.

21. The following F2 results occur from a typical dihybrid cross:

purple:	*A_B_*	9/16
white:	*aaB_*	3/16
white:	*A_bb*	3/16
white:	*aabb*	1/16

If a double heterozygote (*AaBb*) is crossed with a fully recessive organism (*aabb*), what phenotypic ratio is expected in the offspring?

Answer: 3 (white):1 (purple)

22. What types of ratios are likely to occur in crosses (F2) when dealing with two interacting, epistatic gene pairs?

Answer: 9:7, 9:3:4, 12:3:1, 15:1

23. Assume that a cross is made between two organisms, both heterozygous for a gene showing incomplete dominance. What phenotypic and genotypic ratios are expected in the offspring?

Answer: 1:2:1

24. Assume that a dihybrid cross is made in which the genes' loci are autosomal, independently assorting, and incompletely dominant. How many different phenotypes are expected in the offspring?

Answer: 9

Sample Questions: *Chapter 4 Modification of Mendelian Ratios*

25. How many different alleles can a gene have?

Answer: Theoretically, an extremely large number of possibilities exists. Various bases could change, giving a variety of alleles and combinations of those changed bases could provide additional variety.

26. Assume that a dihybrid F2 ratio, resulting from epistasis, was 9:3:4. If a double heterozygote was crossed to the fully recessive type, what phenotypic ratio is expected among the offspring?

Answer: 1:1:2

27. Assume that a dihybrid F2 ratio, resulting from epistasis, was 15:1. If a double heterozygote was crossed to the fully recessive type, what phenotypic ratio is expected among the offspring?

Answer: 3:1

28. Name three modes of inheritance that are influenced by the sex of individuals.

Answer: sex-linked, sex-influenced, sex-limited

29. The white-eye gene in *Drosophila* is recessive and sex-linked. Assume that a white-eyed female is mated to a wild type male. What would be the phenotypes of the offspring?

Answer: females wildtype, males white-eyed

30. Two forms of hemophilia are determined by genes on the X chromosome in humans. Assume that a phenotypically normal woman whose father had hemophilia is married to a normal man. What is the probability that their first son will have hemophilia?

Answer: 1/2

31. Two forms of hemophilia are determined by genes on the X chromosome in humans. Assume that a phenotypically normal woman whose father had hemophilia is married to a normal man. What is the probability that their first daughter will have hemophilia?

Answer: 0

32. State a significant difference between sex-linked and sex-influenced inheritance.

Answer: In sex-linked inheritance, the gene in question is on the X chromosome, while in sex-influenced inheritance, the gene is autosomal.

Sample Questions: Chapter 4   Modification of Mendelian Ratios

33. Pattern baldness is determined by a single autosomal gene pair. When females are homozygous for this gene pair, can they show pattern baldness?

Answer: yes, but the phenotype is less pronounced and is expressed later in life

34. List three examples of sex-influenced inheritance.

Answer: pattern baldness in humans, horn formation in sheep, certain coat patterns in sheep

35. What distinguishes *sex-limited* from *sex-influenced* inheritance?

Answer: In sex-limited inheritance, expression is limited to one sex, while in sex-influenced inheritance, expression differs between the sexes

36. Comb shape in chickens represents one of the classic examples of gene interaction. Two gene pairs interact to influence the shape of the comb. The genes for rose comb (*R*) and pea comb (*P*) together produce walnut comb.   The fully homozygous condition (*rrpp*) produces the single comb. Assume that a rose-comb chicken is crossed with a walnut-comb chicken and the following offspring are produced: 17 walnut, 16 rose, 7 pea, 6 single.   (a) What are the probable genotypes of the parents? (b)   Give the genotypes of each of the offspring classes.

Answers: (a)   *Rrpp*   X   *RrPp*

                      (b)   *R-Pp*   (walnut)
                               R-pp   (rose)
                               rrPp   (pea)
                               rrpp   (single)

37. Many of the color varieties of summer squash are determined by several interacting loci: *AA* or *Aa* give white, *aaBB* or *aaBb* give yellow, and *aabb* produces green. Assume that two fully heterozygous plants are crossed. Give the phenotypes (with frequencies) of the offspring.

Answer: 12 (white) : 3 (yellow): 1(green)

38. A particular cross gives a modified dihybrid ratio of 9:7. What phenotypic ratio would you expect in a testcross of the fully heterozygous F1 crossed with the fully recessive type? Diagram the testcross using *A,a,B,b* symbol sets.

Answer: 3:1

AaBb   X   *aabb*   >   *AaBb, Aabb, aaBb, aabb*

Sample Questions: Chapter 4 Modification of Mendelian Ratios

39. Glucose-6-phosphate dehydrogenase deficiency (G6PD) is inherited as an X-linked recessive gene in humans. A woman whose father suffered from G6PD marries a normal man. (a) What proportion of their sons is expected to be G6PD? (b) If the husband was not normal but was G6PD-deficient, would you change your answer in part (a)?

Answers: (a)   ½
                   (b)   no

40. In a *Drosophila* experiment, a cross was made between homozygous wild type females and yellow-bodied males. All of the resulting F1s were phenotypically wild type. However, adult flies of the F2 generation (resulting from matings of the F1s) had the following characteristics:

Sex	Phenotype	Number
male	wild	123
male	yellow	116
female	wild	240

(a)   Is the mutant gene for yellow body recessive or dominant? State which _____
(b)   Is the yellow locus autosomal or sex-linked? State which_____

Answers:

     (a)   recessive
     (b)   sex-linked.

41. Below is a pedigree of a fairly common human hereditary trait. The boxes represent males and the circles represent females. Shading symbolizes the abnormal phenotype. Given that one gene pair is involved, (a) is the inheritance pattern X-linked or autosomal? (b) Give the genotype of each individual in the pedigree. If more than one genotypic possibility exists, present all possible alternatives.

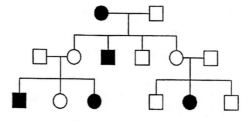

Sample Questions: Chapter 4   Modification of Mendelian Ratios

Answers: (a) autosomal recessive (b)

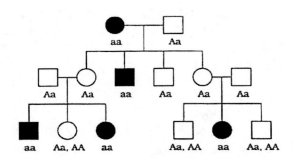

42. The genes for *zeste eyes* and *forked bristles* are located on the X chromosome in *Drosophila melanogaster*. Both genes are recessive. A cross is made between a zest-eyed female and a forked-bristled male. (a) If 200 offspring from this cross were obtained, present the expected number, sex, genotype, and phenotype in each class of the F1.   (b) If the F1 offspring were crossed to produce 800 flies of an F2 generation, present the expected number, sex, and phenotype in each class. Assume no crossing over.

Answers:

(a) $z^+f/z f^+$ =   wild female   (100)
     $z f^+/Y$ =   zeste male   (100)

(b) $z^+f/z f^+$ =   wild female   (200)
     $z f^+/z f^+$ =   zeste female   (200)
     z^+f/Y =   forked male   (200)
     $z f^+/Y$ =   zeste male   (200)

43. In a mating between individuals with the genotypes $I^A I^O$ X $I^O I^O$, what percentage of the offspring are expected to have the O blood type?

Answer: 50%

44. In a mating between individuals with the genotypes $I^A I^B$ X $I^O I^O$, what percentage of the offspring are expected to have the O blood type?

Answer: zero

Sample Questions: Chapter 4 Modification of Mendelian Ratios

45. Erythroblastosis fetalis is a hemolytic disease of the newborn that arises through an interaction of the Rh blood group system. To occur, the mother must be _____ and the father _____.

Answer: Rh-negative, Rh-positive

46. Erythroblastosis fetalis is a hemolytic disease of the newborn that arises through an interaction of the Rh blood group system. To occur, the mother must be Rh-negative and the father Rh-positive. The fetus must be _____.

Answer: Rh-negative, Rh-positive

47. Regarding the ABO blood group system in humans, if an individual is genetically $I^B I^O$ yet expresses the O blood type, it is likely that they have the _____ genotype.

Answer: *hh* (Bombay)

48. Molecular/structural orientations (gradients) in an egg are thought to play a significant role in development. What is the origin of such gradients? What evidence indicates that the maternal genotype is involved in providing such gradients?

Answer: In *Limnaea*, the mother's genotype establishes the direction of the first cleavage division and thus the direction of shell coiling. During formation of the egg, nutritional as well as informational molecules (RNAs) are placed in appropriate positions for development of the embryo. Results (non-Mendelian) indicate that the direction of coiling is determined by the genotype of the mother, not the genotype of the zygote.

49. How are reciprocal crosses used to identify cases of extranuclear inheritance? What criteria would one use to state that a particular mode of inheritance is extranuclear?

Answer: In cases of extrachromosomal inheritance, because the maternal contribution is more significant than the paternal contribution, the results are different from those expected from simple Mendelian inheritance. The traits of the offspring are more influenced by the "maternal" contribution.

50. Name two human disorders that appear to be transmitted extrachromosomally.

Answer: myoclonic epilepsy and Leber's hereditary optic neuropathy

Sample Questions: Chapter 4   Modification of Mendelian Ratios

51.   The inheritance of the petite phenotype in yeast is complicated by an interaction of mitochondrial and nuclear genes. What are these complications? What three categories of petites are commonly described ?

Answer: Both nuclear and cytoplasmic (mitochondrial) genes contribute to the petite phenotype in some cases. The three categories of petites are the following: segregational, neutral, suppressive.

52.   Variegation in four o'clock plants is determined by the phenotype of the ovule source. Why?

Answer: The chloroplasts determine the leaf coloration and the chloroplasts are inherited through the ovule.

53.   How do mitochondria and chloroplasts determine phenotypes? What characteristics of mitochondria and chloroplasts allow such phenotypes to be inherited? Provide specific examples to illustrate your response.

Answer: Both mitochondria and chloroplasts possess DNA, which directs the synthesis of proteins. These proteins influence mitochondrial structure and function and thus influence the phenotype. Mitochondria are involved in energy conversions in cells (petite strains in yeast), while chloroplasts are involved in photosynthesis as well as leaf coloration (iojap in maize).

54. Maternal-effect patterns result when nuclear gene products controlled by the maternal genotype condition the egg and influence early development. Give an example of a maternal effect.

Answer: coiling in *Limnaea*

55. In what way do chloroplast mutations influence the phenotype?

Answer: Chloroplast mutations affect the production of the photosynthetic machinery and/or capabilities of plants, thus influencing the production and utilization of sugars and related energy-rich molecules.

56. In what way do mitochondrial mutations influence the phenotype?

Answer: Mitochondrial mutations affect the production of ATP generated through cellular respiration.

Sample Questions: Chapter 4 Modification of Mendelian Ratios

57. List three criteria indicating that a human disorder may be attributable to genetically altered mitochondria.

Answer: maternal rather than Mendelian inheritance pattern, deficiency in some bioenergetic function of mitochondria, documentation of a specific genetic mutation

58. What three classes of macromolecules are known to be encoded by mtDNA?

Answer: proteins, transfer RNAs, ribosomal RNA

True/False Format

59. With multiple alleles, there can be more than two genetic alternatives for a given locus.

Answer: True

60. With both incomplete dominance and codominance, one expects heterozygous and homozygous classes to be phenotypically identical.

Answer: False

61. The ABO blood group locus in humans provides an example of epistasis.

Answer: False

62. Sex-limited inheritance is the same as sex-linked inheritance.

Answer: False

63. A conditional mutant is one whose expression is influenced by some environmental condition.

Answer: True

64. A typical epistatic ratio is 9:3:4.

Answer: True

65. A 9:7 ratio indicates incomplete dominance.

Answer: False

Sample Questions: Chapter 4 Modification of Mendelian Ratios

66. Pattern baldness and hen/cock feathering in fowl are examples of X-linked inheritance.

Answer: False

67. *Penetrance* specifically refers to the expression of lethal genes in heterozygotes.

Answer: False

68. *Expressivity* is the term used to describe the balanced genetic output from a hemizygous condition.

Answer: False

69. *Hemizygosity* is the term one uses to describe the state of a gene that has no allele on the opposing sex chromosome.

Answer: True

70. *Genomic imprinting* occurs when one allele converts another.

Answer: False

71. *Genomic anticipation* refers to observations that a genetic disorder occurs at an earlier age in successive generations, while *genetic imprinting* occurs when gene expression varies depending on parental origin.

Answer: True

72. Inheritance of the green and white patches phenotype in *Mirabilis jalapa* (four o'clocks) is an example of maternal influence.

Answer: False

73. Mitochondrial mutations are passed equally to offspring by both males and females.

Answer: False

Sample Questions: Chapter 4   Modification of Mendelian Ratios

74. Poky strains in yeast result from suppressive mutations in chloroplast DNA.

Answer: False

75. Direction of shell coiling in *Limnaea peregra* is influenced by a maternal effect.

Answer: True

76. It appears as if the direction of shell coiling in *Limnaea peregra* is influenced by the orientation of the first cleavage division.

Answer: True

77. Genomic imprinting is a form of mitochondrial inheritance.

Answer: False

78. It is safe to say that a maternal effect is caused by the genotype, not the phenotype, of the parent producing the egg.

Answer: True

Chapter 5

Multiple Choice Format

1. Three terms that refer to an individual containing only male *or* female reproductive organism are:

      A.   telomeres, centromeres, and chrommomeres.
      B.   X chromosomes, Y chromosomes, and autosomes.
      C.   unisexual, dioecious, and gonochoric.
      D.   bisexual, monoecious, and hermaphroditic.
      E.   unisexual, monoecious, and hermaphroditic.

Answer: C

2. In humans, the genetic basis for determining the sex "male" is accomplished by the presence of

      A.   a particular portion of the Y chromosome.
      B.   one X chromosome.
      C.   a balance between the number of X chromosomes and the number of haploid sets of autosomes.
      D.   high levels of estrogen.
      E.   multiple alleles scattered throughout the autosomes.

Answer: A

3. Klinefelter syndrome in humans, which leads to underdeveloped testes and sterility, is caused by which chromosomal condition?

      A.   47, XXY
      B.   47, 21+
      C.   45, X
      D.   47, XYY
      E.   triploidy

Answer: A

4. The *Protenor* mode of sex determination is the

      A.   F plasmids inserted into the *FMR*-1 gene.
      B.   XX/XO scheme.
      C.   XO/YY scheme.
      D.   hermaphroditic scheme.
      E.   single translocations in the X chromosome.

Answer: B

5. The *Lygaeus* mode of sex determination is the

      A.   XY/XX scheme.
      B.   XX/XO scheme.
      C.   XO/YY scheme.
      D.   hermaphroditic scheme.
      E.   single translocations in the X chromosome.

Answer: A

Short Answer Format

6. Glucose-6-phosphate dehydrogenase deficiency (G6PD) is inherited as an X-linked recessive gene in humans. A woman whose father suffered from G6PD marries a normal man.

(a) What proportion of their sons is expected to be G6PD?

(b) If the husband was not normal but was G6PD-deficient, would you change your answer in part (a)?

Answer: (a)   1/2,   (b)   no

Sample Questions: Chapter 5 Sex Determination and Sex Chromosomes

7. In *Drosophila*, maleness is determined by the presence of one X chromosome and a normal complement of autosomes; femaleness by two X chromosomes and a normal complement of autosomes. The Y chromosome does not enter into sex determination as in mammals. An individual female fly was observed to be of the XXY chromosome complement (normal autosomal complement) and have white eyes, as contrasted with the normal red eye color of wild type. The female's father had red eyes and the mother had white eyes. Knowing that white eyes is X-linked and recessive, present an explanation for the genetic and chromosomal constitution of the XXY, white-eyed individual. It is important that you state in which parent and at what stage the chromosomal event occurred that caused the genetic and cytogenetic abnormality.

Answer: Nondisjunction could have occurred either at meiosis I or meiosis II in the mother, thus giving the X^wX^wY complement in the offspring.

8. In *Drosophila*, maleness is determined by the presence of one X chromosome and a normal complement of autosomes; femaleness by two X chromosomes and a normal complement of autosomes. An individual female fly was observed to be of the XXY chromosome complement (normal autosomal complement) and have white eyes, as contrasted with the normal red eye color of wild type. The female's mother and father had red eyes. The mother, however, was heterozygous for the gene for *white eyes*. Knowing that *white eyes* is X-linked and recessive, present an explanation for the genetic and chromosomal constitution of the XXY, white eyed individual. It is important that you state in which parent and at what stage the chromosomal event occurred that caused the genetic and cytogenetic abnormality.

Answer: Nondisjunction would have occurred at meiosis II in the mother, thus giving the X^wX^wY complement in the offspring.

9. A color-blind, chromatin-positive male child (one Barr body) has a maternal grandfather who was color blind. The boy's mother and father are phenotypically normal. Construct and support (using appropriately labeled diagrams) a rationale whereby the chromosomal and genetic attributes of the chromatin-positive male are fully explained.

Answer: The female (mother) must be heterozygous and undergo nondisjunction at meiosis II to produce the $X^{rg}X^{rg}Y$ boy.

10. A color-blind woman with Turner syndrome (XO) has a father who is color blind. Given that the gene for the colorblind condition is recessive and X-linked, provide a likely explanation for the origin of the colorblind and cytogenetic conditions in the woman.

Answer: The woman inherited an X^{rg} chromosome from the father. Nondisjunction in the female (at either meiosis I or II) produced an egg with no X chromosome, which, when fertilized by the X^{rg}-bearing sperm, produced the Turner syndrome condition.

Sample Questions: Chapter 5 Sex Determination and Sex Chromosomes

11. In *Drosophila*, maleness is determined by the presence of one X chromosome and a normal complement of autosomes; femaleness by two X chromosomes and a normal complement of autosomes. Give the sex-chromosome constitution (X and Y chromosome) and possible genotypes of offspring resulting from a cross between a white-eyed female ($X^w X^w Y$) and a wild type male (normal chromosome complement) in *Drosophila melanogaster*. Include all zygotic combinations, whether viable or inviable.

Answer:

$X^+ X^w X^w$	=	inviable (dies at third instar stage)
$X^w X^w Y$	=	white-eyed female
$X^+ Y$	=	wildtype male
YY	=	inviable (dies at egg stage)
$X^+ X^w Y$	=	wildtype female
$X^w YY$	=	white-eyed male
$X^+ X^w$	=	wildtype female
$X^w Y$	=	white-eyed male

12. In a *Drosophila* experiment, a cross was made between homozygous wild type females and yellow-bodied males. All of the resulting F1s were phenotypically wild type. However, adult flies of the F2 generation (resulting from matings of the F1s) had the following characteristics:

Sex	Phenotype	Number
male	wild	123
male	yellow	116
female	wild	240

(a)   Is the mutant gene for *yellow body* recessive or dominant?
(b)   Is the *yellow* locus autosomal or sex-linked?

Answer:

(a)   recessive
(b)   sex-linked

Sample Questions: Chapter 5 Sex Determination and Sex Chromosomes

13. In *Drosophila*, maleness is determined by the presence of one X chromosome and a normal complement of autosomes; femaleness by two X chromosomes and a normal complement of autosomes. Give the sex of the following organisms assuming that the autosomes are present in the normal number.

Sex Chromosome Complement	Organism	
	Humans	Drosophila
XX	_____	_____
XY	_____	_____
XO	_____	_____
XXX	_____	_____
XXY	_____	_____

Answer:

Sex Chromosome Complement	Organism	
	Humans	Drosophila
XX	female	female
XY	male	male
XO	female	male
XXX	female	female
XXY	male	female

14. Dosage compensation leads to a variety of interesting coat color patterns in certain mammals. For instance, a female cat that is heterozygous for two coat color alleles, say black and orange, will usually have the "calico" or mosaic phenotype. Describe the chromosomal basis for the mosaicism (calico) in the female. Explain why chromosomally normal male cats do not show the mosaic phenotype but XXY male cats can be "calico."

Answer: Because of dosage compensation, one of the X chromosomes randomly "turns off" early in development. Once such a chromosome is inactivated, it remains so in daughter cells. Recessive genes on the remaining active X chromosome are expressed because their allele (on the inactive X chromosome) is not capable of expression. Because males typically have only one X chromosome, X chromosome inactivation does not occur; however, in XXY males, which are heterozygous for certain coat color genes, such inactivation and therefore mosaicism is possible.

Sample Questions: Chapter 5 Sex Determination and Sex Chromosomes

15. Below is a pedigree of a fairly common human hereditary trait. The boxes represent males and circles, represent females. Shading symbolizes the abnormal phenotype. Given that one gene pair is involved,

(a) is the inheritance pattern X-linked or autosomal?

(b) Give the genotype of each individual in the pedigree. If more than one genotypic possibility exists, present all possible alternatives.

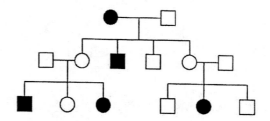

Answers: (a) autosomal recessive

(b)

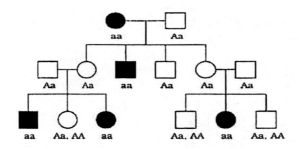

16. List three abnormalities involving numbers of X chromosomes.

Answer: Klinefelter syndrome, Turner syndrome, XXXX syndrome

17. Individuals have been identified who have two different karyotypes, such as 45,X/46,XY or 45,X/46,XX. Such individuals are called

Answer: mosaics

18. What particular karyotype was at one time considered to be related to criminal predisposition?

Answer: XYY

Sample Questions: Chapter 5 Sex Determination and Sex Chromosomes

19. A small part of the human Y chromosome contains the gene which is responsible for determining maleness. What is the name of this gene?

Answer: SRY (sex-determining region Y)

20. Under what condition might a female have the XY sex chromosome complement?

Answer: The individual has one complete X chromosome and a Y chromosome, which lacks SRY.

21. How many Barr bodies would one expect to see in cells of Turner syndrome females and Klinefelter syndrome males?

Answer: zero and one, respectively

22. Phenotypic mosaicism for X-linked genes in female mammals can be caused by what mechanism?

Answer: dosage compensation involving the X chromosome

23. In *Drosophila*, maleness is determined by the presence of one X chromosome and a normal complement of autosomes; femaleness by two X chromosomes and a normal complement of autosomes. Assuming a normal number of autosomes, what would be the sex of the following? XXY mouse, XXY *Drosophila*

Answer: male and female, respectively

24. Give an example of an organism in which the male is not the heterogametic sex.

Answer: moths, butterflies, some fish, most birds, reptiles, amphibians, and at least one species of plants (*Fragaria orientalis*)

25. In *Drosophila*, maleness is determined by the presence of one X chromosome and a normal complement of autosomes; femaleness by two X chromosomes and a normal complement of autosomes. In *Drosophila*, the sex of a fly with the following karyotype, XO:2A, is

Answer: male (sterile)

Sample Questions: Chapter 5   Sex Determination and Sex Chromosomes

26. While triple-X human females typically have normal offspring, what kinds of gametes, with respect to the X chromosomes, would you expect from such XXX females? Draw meiotic stages showing the gametes that are expected to be produced.

Answer:

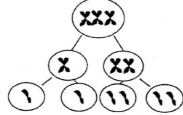

27. Dosage compensation in mammals typically involves the random inactivation of one of the two X chromosomes relatively early in development. Such X-chromosome inactivation often leads to phenotypic mosaicism. Assume that black fur in cats is due to the X-linked recessive gene *b,* while its dominant allele *B* produces yellow fur. A *Bb* heterozygote is a mosaic called "tortoise shell" or "calico." Using appropriate gene symbols, diagram a mating between a black male and a "calico" female. Give the phenotypes and genotypes of all the offspring.

Answer: *b*Y   X   *Bb*   =

   Bb (calico female), *bb* (black female), *B*Y (yellow male), *b*Y (black male)

28. Klinefelter and Turner syndromes have how many chromosomes, respectively?

Answer: 47, 45

29. Studies done in the 1960s suggested that individuals with the XYY were prone to criminal behavior. What conclusions presently seem appropriate concerning this chromosomal condition?

Answer: There is a high, but not constant, correlation between the extra Y chromosome and the predisposition of males to behavioral problems.

30. Describe an experiment in which transgenic mice were used to identify the male-determining region of the Y chromosome.

Answer: When DNA containing only the mouse *Sry* is injected into normal XX mouse eggs, most of the offspring develop into males.

31. Describe various genetic regions of the human Y chromosome.

Answer: PARs = pseudoautosomal regions, NRY = nonrecombining region of the Y, SRY = sex-determining region

32. What is the composition of a Barr body?

Answer: X chromosome

True/False Format

33. Normally in humans, all the sons of a male showing a sex-linked phenotype will inherit the trait.

Answer: False

34. Normally in humans, all the sons of a female homozygous for a sex-linked recessive gene will inherit that trait.

Answer: True

35. Sex-influenced genes are those that cause males to be males and females to be females.

Answer: False

36. Sex-limited genes are those that cause males to be males and females to be females.

Answer: False

37. In chickens, the male is the homogametic sex.

Answer: True

Sample Questions: Chapter 5   Sex Determination and Sex Chromosomes

38. An individual with Klinefelter syndrome generally has one Barr body.

Answer: True

39. An individual with Turner Syndrome has no Barr bodies.

Answer: True

40. A typical XX human female has one Barr body.

Answer: True

41.   In humans, the male is the homogametic sex.

Answer: False

42. In *Drosophila*, the female is the heterogametic sex.

Answer: False

43. Dosage compensation is accomplished in humans by inactivation of the Y chromosome.

Answer: False

Chapter 6

Multiple Choice Format

1. Quantitative inheritance involves the interaction of a number of gene loci. The pattern of genetic transmission typical of quantitative inheritance is

        A.   discontinuous distributions such as 3:1.
        B.   typical of Mendelian inheritance.
        C.   continuous variation of phenotypic expression.
        D.   a 9:3:3:1 ratio.
        E.   usually a pattern that clearly reflects dominance and recessiveness.

Answer: C

2. Assume that a cross is made between tall and dwarf tobacco plants. The F1 generation showed intermediate height, while the F2 generation showed a distribution of height ranging from tall to dwarf, like the original parents, and many heights between the extremes. These data are consistent with which mode of inheritance?

        A.   multiple-factor inheritance
        B.   alternation of generations
        C.   codominance
        D.   incomplete dominance
        E.   hemizygosity

Answer: A

3. Bell-shaped distributions produced by plotting results of F2 and F3 crosses are typical of what type of inheritance?

        A.   multiple-factor inheritance
        B.   alternation of generations
        C.   codominance
        D.   incomplete dominance
        E.   hemizygosity

Answer: A

Sample Questions: Chapter 6   Quantitative Genetics

4. Characteristics exhibited by continuously varying traits include

A.   sex-linked genes only.
B.   autosomal genes only.
C.   quantification by measuring, weighing, counting, etc.
D.   a 9:3:3:1 ratio.
E.   3:1, 1:1 ratios.

Answer: C

5. Environmental factors typically influence inheritance of

A.   multiple alleles.
B.   codominance.
C.   trihybrid crosses.
D.   polygenic traits.
E.   dominantly inherited traits.

Answer: D

Short Answer Format

6. Huntington disease is inherited in humans as an autosomal dominant gene. Affected individuals show progressive brain deterioration from cell death in the cerebral cortex. Onset of the disease usually occurs between ages 30 and 50. Give two possible reasons for the observed variation in the age of onset of this disease.

Answer: variable genetic background, internal physiological environment, external environment

7. In the analysis of quantitative traits, positions on chromosomes called quantitative trait loci (QTLs) are often discussed. In the same context, restriction fragment length polymorphisms (RFLPs) are also discussed. What is the relationship between QTLs and RFLPs?

Answer: In many organisms, traditional genetic markers are not available for the mapping of regions of chromosomes containing genes responsible for determining quantitative traits (QTLs). DNA polymorphisms generate molecular markers (RFLPs) that can serve as reference points in mapping QTLs.

Sample Questions: Chapter 6   Quantitative Genetics

8. List at least two statistical terms commonly used in the analysis of quantitative traits.

Answer: mean, variance, standard deviation, standard error of the mean

9. Define the term *broad-sense heritability*. What is implied by a relatively high value of H^2? Express aspects of broad-sense heritability in equation form.

Answer: Broad-sense heritability (H^2) refers to the degree to which phenotypic variation is due to genetic factors.   A very high value indicates that the environment had a relatively low impact on phenotypic variation. $V_P = V_E + V_G + V_{GE}$

10. Describe the value of using twins in the study of questions relating the relative impact of heredity versus environment.

Answer: Monozygotic twins are derived from the splitting of a single fertilized egg and are therefore of identical genetic makeup. When such twins are raised in the same versus different settings, an estimate of relative hereditary and environmental influences can often be made.

11. In the early part of the 1900s, Nilsson-Ehle, East, and others described experiments demonstrating showed that multiple loci may be involved in the inheritance of certain traits. Such patterns are often called

Answer: polygenic traits, multiple factor inheritance

12. If the proportion of F2 individuals resembling either of the two most extreme phenotypes (the parental phenotypes) can be determined, what formula can be applied to determine the number of gene pairs involved?

Answer: $1/4^n$ (where n is the number of gene pairs)

13. What formula can be used to determine the number of categories (phenotypes) possible in the F2 results of a polygenic system?

Answer: $2n + 1$ (where n is the number of gene pairs)

14. Assume that in the F2 of a series of crosses, 1/64 of the offspring resemble one of the parents (P). How many gene pairs are involved in producing these results?

Answer: 3

15. Assume that four polygenic gene pairs are involved in determining phenotypes of F2. How many phenotypic classes are expected?

Answer: 9

Sample Questions: Chapter 6   Quantitative Genetics

16. During the nineteenth century, Sir Francis Galton investigated various diameters of sweet peas. From these and other studies came the foundation for the field of genetics called_____.

Answer: quantitative or polygenic inheritance

17. Name the field of study first devised by Galton early in this century to assess the inheritance of traits exhibiting continuous variation.

Answer: biometry

18. List three statistical values often used to represent a sample.

Answer: b.ean, standard deviation, standard error, variance

19. Given the following numbers, calculate the mean: 10, 12, 14, 16, 18

Answer: 14

20. What is the name and formula for describing sample variability?

Answer: variance, $s^2 = S(X_i - X)^2/n-1$

21. To estimate how much the means of a variety of like samples drawn from the same population might vary, what statistic is often used?

Answer: standard error of the mean ($S_x = s/\sqrt{n}$)

22. If one is attempting to determine the influence of genes or the environment on phenotypic variation, inbred strains with individuals of a relatively homogeneous or constant genetic background are often used. Variation observed between different inbred strains reared in a constant or homogeneous environment would likely be caused by genetic factors, while variation observed among members of the same inbred strain reared under varying environmental conditions would likely be caused by what source?

Answer: nongenetic factors generally categorized as "environmental"

23. What is the formal expression used to examine the relative importance of genetic versus environmental factors?

Answer: Heritability index (H^2) = V_G/V_P

Sample Questions: Chapter 6   Quantitative Genetics

24. Name the three components that add to give phenotypic variance.

Answer: environmental variance (V_E), genetic variance (V_G), and variance resulting from the interaction of genetics and environment (V_{GE})

25. Interpret the meaning of an H^2 value (broad-sense heritability) that approaches 1.0.

Answer: Almost all the phenotypic variation is determined by heredity.

26. Interpret the meaning of an H^2 value (broad-sense heritability) that approaches 0.0.

Answer: Almost all the phenotypic variation is determined by the environment.

27. Provide brief definitions for the terms *additive variance*, *dominance variance*, and *interactive variance*.

Answer: Additive variance results form the average effect of additive genes. Dominance variance accounts for variation when phenotypic expression in heterozygotes is not precisely intermediate between the two homozygotes. Interactive variance occurs when two or more loci behave epistatically.

28. Provide a formal equation for h^2 (narrow-sense heritability).

Answer: $h^2 = V_A/V_P$

29. What is the relationship between the narrow-sense heritability index (h^2) and the impact of selection?

Answer: A relatively high h^2 value is a prediction of a significant impact that selection may have in altering an initial population.

30. Name two mammalian traits with relatively high heritability (h^2) values and two with relatively low h^2 values.

Answer: high h^2: tail length in mice, birth weight in cattle; low h^2: litter size in mice and conception rate in cattle

31. Regarding twin studies in mammals, distinguish between the terms *concordant* and *discordant*.

Answer: Concordant refers to a given trait expressed similarly between twins; discordant refers to a case in which one member of the twin pair expresses the trait while the other does not.

Sample Questions: Chapter 6 Quantitative Genetics

32. Name two human traits that would be expected to have a very high concordance.

Answer: eye color, blood type

33. What are QTLs and RFLPs?

Answer: QTLs are quantitative trait loci and refer to genes controlling the expression of quantitative traits. RFLPs are restriction fragment length polymorphisms.

34. Provide a brief description of both phenomena: *discontinuous inheritance* and *continuous inheritance*. How are the two related, how are they different?

Answer: At the transmission level one sees "step-wise" distributions in discontinuous inheritance but "smoother" or more bell-shaped distributions in continuous inheritance, as shown below:

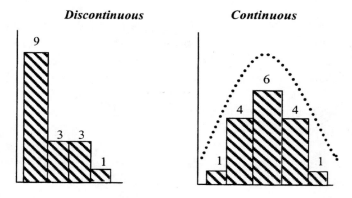

Both patterns are formed from normal Mendelian principles of segregation and independent assortment. The differences are in the manner in which the gene products interact; continuous inheritance involves additive effects.

35. Continuous inheritance is often related to the term *quantitative inheritance*. Why?

Answer: In continuous inheritance, we consider each involved locus as having a quantitative input on the production of a single characteristic of the phenotype. In addition, although it may not always be the case, we would consider each gene product as being qualitatively similar.

Sample Questions: Chapter 6   Quantitative Genetics

36. What is meant by the term *heritability*? Describe the components of heritability, and provide a brief explanation of each. Of what interest is heritability to animal and plant breeders?

Answer: Heritability refers to the degree to which observed phenotypic variation for a given trait is inherited. Components are environmental variance, genetic variance, and interaction of the two. From information on heritability, breeders can determine the degree of improvement to expect from selective breeding.

37. Individuals with the same genetic background and a high degree of homozygosity are said to be *isogenic*. Of what value are isogenic strains in genetic studies?

Answer: Because the genetic background is the same (or at least very similar), phenotypic variation must be due to nongenetic factors.

38. What is meant by the genetic background of an organism? What influence does genetic background have over the phenotype of the organism?

Answer: The genetic background of an organism usually refers to the entire genetic complement of an organism except for the gene (or genes) under study. Genetic background may have a profound influence over gene expression, depending on the molecular/developmental environment in which a gene is being expressed.

39. How would the use of a large series of monozygotic and dizygotic twins enhance studies on the genetic basis of human behavior?

Answer: Monozygotic twins are genetically identical; when reared under the same versus different environments, one can estimate the degree to which variation in behavior is determined by heredity. Dizygotic twins are genetically different, but by having the same intrauterine and developing environment (if being reared in the same household), one can again estimate the influence of heredity on behavioral traits.

40. Assume that you are studying a trait determined by a number of polygenes. If there are seven phenotypic categories, how many genes are probably involved?

Answer: three gene pairs

41. The 9:3:3:1 ratio is typical of a dihybrid cross where complete dominance and independent assortment occur. What is the dihybrid ratio with independent assortment of polygenes?

Answer: 1:4:6:4:1

42. How many gene pairs are involved in generating a typical 1:4:6:4:1 ratio?

Answer: 2

Sample Questions: Chapter 6   Quantitative Genetics

43. What is the name of the process of selecting a specific group of organisms from an initially heterogeneous population for future breeding purposes?

Answer: artificial selection

44. A "marker" in a genetic sense usually represents a site along a chromosome where a specific nucleotide sequence exists. What specific phrase is used when such markers are identified by restriction endonucleases and a particular set of DNA fragments is generated?

Answer: restriction fragment length polymorphism (RFLP)

True/False Format

45. Polygenes are genes involved in determining continuously varying or multiple-factor traits.

Answer: True

46. Additive alleles are alleles that are epistatic over nonallelic genes which influence the same phenotypic characteristic.

Answer: False

47. The multiple factor hypothesis suggests that many factors or genes contribute to the phenotype in a cumulative or quantitative manner.

Answer: True

48. Concordance refers to the frequency with which members of a twin pair express a different trait.

Answer: False

49. Heritability is a measure of the degree to which the phenotypic variation of a given trait is due to genetic factors.

Answer: True

50. Traits such as height, general body structure, skin color, and some behavioral traits are probably caused primarily by genes that behave codominantly or epistatically.

Answer: False

Chapter 7

Multiple Choice Format

1. When an organism gains or loses one or more chromosomes but not a complete haploid set, the condition is known as

     A.   polyploidy.
     B.   euploidy.
     C.   aneuploidy.
     D.   triploidy.
     E.   trisomy.

Answer: C

2. The condition known as *cri-du-chat syndrome* in humans has a genetic constitution designated as

     A.   45, X.
     B.   heteroplasmy.
     C.   46, 5p-.
     D.   triploidy.
     E.   trisomy.

Answer: C

3. While the most frequent forms of Down syndrome are caused by a random error, nondisjunction of chromosome #21, Down syndrome occasionally runs in families. The cause of this form of familial Down syndrome is

     A.   an inversion involving chromosome #21.
     B.   a chromosomal aberration involving chromosome #1.
     C.   too many X chromosomes.
     D.   a translocation between chromosome #21 and a member of the D chromosome group.
     E.   a maternal age effect.

Answer: D

4. A genomic condition that may be responsible for some forms of fragile-X syndrome as well as Huntington disease involves

      A.   F plasmids inserted into the *FMR*-1 gene.
      B.   various lengths of trinucleotide repeats.
      C.   multiple breakpoints fairly evenly dispersed along the X chromosome.
      D.   multiple inversions in the X chromosome.
      E.   single translocations in the X chromosome.

Answer: B

5. Recently, a gene located on chromosome #3 in humans, *FHIT*, has been shown to be associated with the significant human malady known as

      A.   cancer.
      B.   Huntington disease.
      C.   "mad cow" disease.
      D.   Klinefelter syndrome.
      E.   XYY/XY mosacism.

Answer: A

Short Answer Format

6. What explanation is generally given for lethality of monosomic individuals?

Answer: Monosomy may unmask recessive lethals that are tolerated in heterozygotes carrying the wildtype allele.

7. Describe the maternal age effect associated with Down syndrome.

Answer: For unknown reasons, the nondisjunctional event that produces Down syndrome occurs more frequently during oogenesis in women older than age 35.

8. Name two methods used in genetic prenatal diagnostic testing in humans.

Answer: Amniocentesis and chorionic villus sampling (CVS)

Sample Questions: Chapter 7 Chromosome Mutations: Variations in Chromosome Number and Arrangement

9. What is polyploid condition resulting from the addition of one or more extra sets of chromosomes, identical to the normal haploid complement of the same species?

Answer: autotetraploidy

10. Colchicine is an alkyloid derived from plants. What is its effect on chromosome behavior?

Answer: By interfering with spindle formation, replicated chromosomes fail to migrate to the poles at anaphase; thus, sister chromatids end up in the same nucleus.

11. Deletions are chromosomal aberrations in which some portion of a chromosome is missing. Describe a method, using deletions, to determine the actual, physical location of a gene.

Answer: If one is using *Drosophila*, an example of the method would be as follows. Cross homozygous mutant flies to homozygous wildtype flies that have been irradiated (or those with a series of known deletions). Select mutant flies in the F1. Those flies of the F1 that display the mutant phenotype may have resulted from the wildtype allele being deleted by the X-ray treatment. Establish a stock of the exceptional mutant fly, then examine polytene chromosomes in larvae. The mutation in question may be contained in the compensation loop in the homologue of the deleted chromosome. If a series of known deletions is available (and these do exist in stock centers throughout the world), one could test (by the mating described above) the mutation against each deletion. Obviously this would be a very time-consuming task unless one had some prior knowledge about the general location of the mutant gene. This can be accomplished using balancer chromosomes and standard linkage determination. Once the mutant gene is "exposed" by a given deletion, a series of additional deletions can be used to "fine map" the region and determine a fairly accurate location for the gene.

12. Inversion heterokaryotypes are often characterized as having reduced crossing over and reduced fertility. Assume that you were examining a strain of organisms you knew to be inversion heterokaryotypes and saw a relatively high number of double chromatid bridges extending between anaphase I nuclei. What would be a likely explanation for this observation? Explain with a labeled diagram.

Answer: A four-strand double crossover in the inversion loop of a paracentric inversion (in the heterozygous state) would generate the double bridge and two acentric fragments (which would be lost).

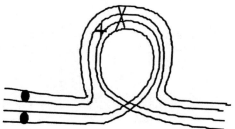

13.   Clearly illustrate the pairing configuration of an inversion (paracentric) heterokaryotype.

Answer: The pairing of homologous chromosomes of an inversion heterokaryotype is typically one of an outside loop filled by an inside loop.

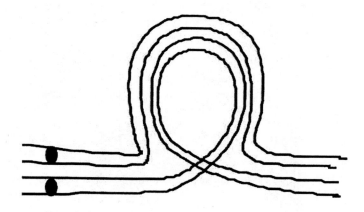

14.   Given that a human normally contains 46 chromosomes, give the chromosome number for each of the conditions listed below:

>   Turner syndrome (female, no Barr bodies)
>   Klinefelter syndrome (male, one Barr body)
>   triploid
>   Down syndrome (trisomic)
>   trisomy 13

Answer:

        Turner syndrome (female, no Barr bodies)   45
        Klinefelter syndrome (male, one Barr body) 47
        triploid69
        Down syndrome (trisomic)   47
        trisomy 13   47

15. What is meant by the terms *acentric* and *dicentric*?

Answer: A chromosome without a centromere is called acentric, while a chromosome with two centromeres is called dicentric.

16. Under what circumstance can an individual with Down syndrome have 46 chromosomes?

Answer: If the person carries a D/G translocation, such as 14/21.

17. Fragile-X syndrome (or Martin-Bell syndrome) is the most common form of inherited mental retardation in humans. Is it more common in males or females? What is *FMR*-1?

Answer: It is more common in males (1/1250). *FMR*-1 is one of a growing number of genes where a sequence of three nucleotides is repeated many times, expanding the size of the gene.

18. What is meant by the acronym *rDNA*?

Answer: rDNA encodes rRNA

19. Provide an example of gene redundancy that occurs in both eukaryotes and prokaryotes.

Answer: rDNA

20. Trisomics are observed in humans while monosomics are not. Why?

Answer: Monosomics are inviable.

Sample Questions: *Chapter 7 Chromosome Mutations: Variations in Chromosome Number and Arrangement*

True/False Format

21. Doubling the chromosomes of a sterile species hybrid with colchicine or cold shock is a method of producing a fertile species hybrid (amphidiploid).

Answer: True

22. Assume a species has a diploid chromosome number of 24. The term applied to an individual with 36 chromosomes is *triploid*.

Answer: True

23. Assume a species has a diploid chromosome number of 24. The term applied to an individual with 25 chromosomes is *triploid*.

Answer: False

24. An expected meiotic pairing configuration in a triploid would be a trivalent.

Answer: True

25. An individual with Patau syndrome would be called a triploid.

Answer: False

26. The term *aneuploidy* is synonymous with the term *segmental deletion*.

Answer: False

27. Nondisjunction is viewed as a major cause of aneuploidy.

Answer: True

Sample Questions: Chapter 7 Chromosome Mutations: Variations in Chromosome Number and Arrangement

28. Individuals with familial Down syndrome are trisomic and have 47 chromosomes.

Answer: False

29. Familial Down syndrome is caused by a translocation involving chromosome #21.

Answer: True

30. Chorionic villus sampling (CVS) is sometimes preferred to amniocentesis because results can be provided earlier in the pregnancy.

Answer: True

31. In *Drosophila melanogaster* ($2n = 8$), a fly with seven chromosomes could be called a haplo-IV.

Answer: True

32. A deletion may set up a genetic circumstance known as overdominance.

Answer: False

33. A pericentric inversion includes the centromere.

Answer: True

34. Assume that an organism has a diploid chromosome number of 14. There would be 28 chromosomes in a tetraploid.

Answer: True

35. An autotriploid may arise by trispermic fertilization.

Answer: False

Sample Questions: Chapter 7 Chromosome Mutations: Variations in Chromosome Number and Arrangement

36. Assume that an organism has a haploid chromosome number of 7. There would be 14 chromosomes in a monoploid individual of that species.

Answer: False

37. A position effect occurs when a gene's expression is altered by virtue of a change in its position. One might expect position effects to occur with inversions and translocations.

Answer: True

38. Gene duplications provide an explanation for the origin of gene families.

Answer: True

39. rDNA in eukaryotes is typically redundant.

Answer: True

40. A paracentric inversion is one whose breakpoints do not flank the centromere.

Answer: True

41. Inversions suppress crossing over by providing a chemical imbalance because of breakpoints within certain genes.

Answer: False

42. Translocations may be pericentric or paracentric.

Answer: False

43. Inversions and translocations are without evolutionary significance.

Answer: False

Sample Questions: Chapter 7 Chromosome Mutations: Variations in Chromosome Number and Arrangement

44. In general, inversion and translocation heterozygotes are as fertile as organisms whose chromosome are in the standard arrangement.

Answer: False

45. When an extra chromosome is present, the term *triploid* is appropriate.

Answer: False

46. Organisms with inversions and translocations are *tetraploid*.

Answer: False

47. A tetraploid organisms has a $4n$ chromosome complement.

Answer: True

Sample Questions: Chapter 8 Linkage and Chromosome Mapping in Eukaryotes

Chapter 8

Multiple Choice Format

1. When two genes fail to assort independently, the term normally applied is

        A.   discontinuous inheritance.
        B.   Mendelian inheritance.
        C.   linkage.
        D.   tetrad analysis.
        E.   dominance and/or recessiveness.

Answer: C

2. Assume that a cross is made between *AaBb* and *aabb* plants and all the offspring are either *AaBb* or *aabb*. These results are consistent with the following circumstance:

        A.   complete linkage
        B.   alternation of generations
        C.   codominance
        D.   incomplete dominance
        E.   hemizygosity

Answer: A

3. Assume that a cross is made between *AaBb* and *aabb* plants and the offspring fall into approximately equal numbers of the following groups: *AaBb, Aabb, aaBb, aabb*. These results are consistent with the following circumstance:

        A.   independent assortment
        B.   alternation of generations
        C.   complete linkage
        D.   incomplete dominance
        E.   hemizygosity

Answer: A

Sample Questions: Chapter 8 Linkage and Chromosome Mapping in Eukaryotes

4. Assume that a cross is made between *AaBb* and *aabb* plants and the offspring occur in the following numbers: 106 *AaBb*, 48 *Aabb*, 52 *aaBb*, 94 *aabb*. These results are consistent with the following circumstance:

      A.   sex-linked inheritance with 30 % crossing over
      B.   linkage with 50% crossing over
      C.   linkage with approximately 33 map units between the two gene loci
      D.   independent assortment
      E.   100% recombination

Answer: C

5. Assume that, regarding a particular gene, one scored 30 second division ascospore arrangements and 70 first division arrangements in *Neurospora*. What would be the map distance between the gene and the centromere?

      A.   30
      B.   60
      C.   70
      D.   15
      E.   insufficient information provided to answer this question

Answer: D

6. The phenomenon in which one crossover decreases the likelihood of crossovers in nearby regions is called

      A.   chiasma.
      B.   negative interference.
      C.   reciprocal genetic exchange.
      D.   positive interference.
      E.   mitotic recombination.

Answer: D

Sample Questions: Chapter 8   Linkage and Chromosome Mapping in Eukaryotes

7. Methods for determining the linkage group and genetic map in humans involve which of the following?

      A.   syntenic testing and lod score determination
      B.   twin spots and tetrad analysis
      C.   tetrad analysis and bromodeozyuridine
      D.   zygotene and pachytene DNA synthesis
      E.   chiasmatype and classical analyses

Answer: A

Short Answer Format

8. The genes for mahogany eyes and ebony body are approximately 25 map units apart on chromosome #3 in *Drosophila*. Assume that a mahogany-eyed female was mated to an ebony-bodied male and the resulting F1 phenotypically wildtype females were mated to mahogany, ebony males. Of 1000 offspring, what would be the expected phenotypes and in what numbers?

Answer: mahogany = 375; ebony = 375; wild type = 125; mahogany-ebony = 125

9. Assume that there are 12 map units between two loci in the mouse and that you are able to microscopically observe meiotic chromosomes in this organism. If you examined 200 primary oocytes, in how many would you expect to see a chiasma between the two loci mentioned above?

Answer: 48

10. Diagram chromosomal events that provide for segregation of alleles (*A* and *a*) during meiosis II.

Answer:

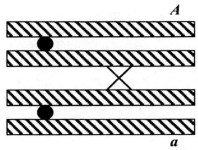

89

Sample Questions: Chapter 8 Linkage and Chromosome Mapping in Eukaryotes

11. Given that loci *A* and *B* in *Drosophila* are sex-linked and 20 map units apart, what phenotypic frequencies would you expect in male and female offspring resulting from the following crosses? (Assume *A* and *B* are dominant to *a* and *b*, respectively.)

(a)   *AaBb* (*cis*) female X *ab*/Y male
(b)   *AaBb* (*trans*) X *ab*/Y male
(c)   *aabb* female X *AB*/Y male

Answer:

(a) $AB = 40$; $ab = 40$; $Ab = 10$; $aB = 10$ (sexes have the same phenoytpes)
(b) $Ab = 40$; $aB = 40$; $AB = 10$; $ab = 10$ (sexes have the same phenotypes)
(c)   all males $= ab$; all females $= AB$

12. Phenotypically wild F1 female *Drosophila*, whose mothers had light eyes (*lt*) and fathers had straw (*stw*) bristles produced the following offspring when crossed to homozygous light-straw males:

Phenotype	Number
light-straw	22
wild	18
light	990
straw	970
Total	2000

Compute the map distance between the *light* and *straw* loci.

Answer: 2 map units

13. Assume that the genes for *tan body* and *bare wings* are 15 map units apart on chromosome #2 in *Drosophila*. Assume also that a tan-bodied, bare-winged female was mated to a wildtype male and the resulting F1 phenotypically wildtype females were mated to tan-bodied, bare-winged males. Of 1000 offspring, what would be the expected phenotypes and in what numbers?

Answer: wild type $= 425$; tan-bare $= 425$; tan $= 75$; bare $= 75$

Sample Questions: Chapter 8 Linkage and Chromosome Mapping in Eukaryotes

14. Assume that investigators crossed a strain of flies carrying the dominant eye mutation *Lobe* on the second chromosome to a strain homozygous for the second chromosome recessive mutations *smooth abdomen* and *straw body*. The F1 Lobe females were then backcrossed to homozygous smooth abdomen, straw body males, and the following phenotypes were observed:

smooth abdomen, straw body	820
Lobe	780
smooth abdomen, Lobe	42
straw body	58
smooth abdomen	148
Lobe, straw body	152

(a) Give the gene sequence and map units between these three loci.
(b) What is the coefficient of coincidence?

Answer:

(a)   Lobe is in the middle:

   smooth abdomen---5---Lobe-----------15-------------straw body

(b)   zero

15. In *Drosophila*, assume that the gene for *scute bristles* (*s*) is located at map position 0.0 and the gene for *ruby eyes* (*r*) is at position 15.0. Both genes are located on the X chromosome and are recessive to their wildtype alleles. A cross is made between scute-bristled females and ruby-eyed males. Phenotypically wild F1 females were then mated to homozygous double mutant males and 1000 offspring were produced. Give the phenotypes and frequencies expected.

Answer: scute = 425; ruby = 425; wild type = 75; scute-ruby = 75

16. Assume that a cross is made between *AaBb* and *aabb* plants and the offspring occur in the following numbers: 106 *AaBb*, 48 *Aabb*, 52 *aaBb*, 94 *aabb*. These results are consistent with the following arrangement of genes:

Answer: In the *AaBb* parent, the dominant genes are on one homolog and the recessive genes are on the other.

Sample Questions: Chapter 8 Linkage and Chromosome Mapping in Eukaryotes

17. In the fruit fly *Drosophila melanogaster* a spineless (no wing bristles) female fly is mated to a male that is claret (dark eyes) and hairless (no thoracic bristles). Phenotypically wildtype F1 female progeny were mated to fully homozygous (mutant) males, and the following progeny (1000 total) were observed:

Phenotypes	Number Observed
spineless	321
wild	38
claret, spineless	130
claret	18
claret, hairless	309
hairless, claret, spineless	32
hairless	140
hairless, spineless	12

(a) Which gene is in the middle?

(b) With respect to the three genes mentioned in the problem, what are the genotypes of the homozygous parents used in making the phenotypically wild F1 heterozygote?

(c) What are the map distances between the three genes? A correct formula with the values plugged in for each distance will be sufficient.

(d) What is the coefficient of coincidence? A correct formula with the values plugged in will be sufficient.

Answer:

(a) *hairless*

(b) *cl h +/cl h +   and + + sp/+ + sp*

(c) *cl-------30-----h---10---sp*

(d) .03/.03 = 1

Sample Questions: Chapter 8 Linkage and Chromosome Mapping in Eukaryotes

18. Three loci, *mitochondrial malate dehydrogenase* forms *a* and *b* (*MDHa, MDHb*), *glucouronidase* forms *1, 2* (*GUS1, GUS2*), and a *histone* gene forms +, - (*H⁺, H⁻*) are located on chromosome #7 in humans. Assume that the *MDH* locus is at position 35, *GUS* at position 45, and *H* at position 75. A female whose mother was homozygous for *MDHa, GUS2*, and *H⁺* and whose father was homozygous for *MDHb, GUS1*, and *H⁻* produces a sample of 1000 egg cells. Give the genotypes and expected numbers of the various types of cells she would produce. Assume no chromosomal interference.

Answer:

MDHa	*GUS2*	H^+	=	315	*MDHa*	*GUS2*	H^-	=	135
MDHb	*GUS1*	H^-	=	315	*MDHb*	*GUS1*	H^+	=	135
MDHa	*GUS1*	H^-	=	35	*MDHa*	*GUS1*	H^+	=	15
MDHb	*GUS2*	H^+	=	35	*MDHb*	*GUS2*	H^-	=	15

19. To what scientific activities do the terms *synkaryon* and *heterokaryon* refer?

Answer: cell (heterokaryon) and nuclear (synkaryon) fusion and gene mapping in eukaryotes

20. (a) In a three-point mapping experiment, what three general classes of offspring are expected (assuming crossovers occur)? (b) How many different genotypic classes are expected?

Answer: (a) Non-crossovers, single crossovers, double crossovers; (b) 8

21. What is the expected evolutionary significance of genetic recombination?

Answer: production of genetic variation

22. Assume that two genes are 80 map units apart on chromosome #2 of *Drosophila* and a cross is made between a doubly heterozygous female and a homozygous recessive male. What percent recombination would be expected in the offspring of this type of cross?

Answer: 50 (maximum)

23. Provide a brief definition for the term *positive interference*.

Answer: A crossover in one region decreases the likelihood of crossovers in nearby regions.

Sample Questions: Chapter 8 Linkage and Chromosome Mapping in Eukaryotes

24. Two lines of research indicated that crossing over actually involves the breakage and reunion of chromatid material. What organisms were involved and who did the work?

Answer: Creighton and McClintock (corn) and Stern (*Drosophila*)

25. What advantage is BUdR (bromodeoxyuridine) in the study of chromosome structure and recombination?

Answer: Chromatids stained with BUdR in both DNA strands are distinguishable from those with BUdR in only one strand of the double helix.

26. Sister chromatid exchanges increase in frequency in the presence of X rays, certain viruses, ultraviolet light, and certain chemical mutagens. In what autosomal recessive disorder is there known to be an increase in sister chromatid exchanges?

Answer: Bloom syndrome

27. Under what circumstance might two loci be on the same chromosome but behave as if independently assorting in crosses?

Answer: If the genes are far apart, they may show independent assortment.

28. In the early 1900s, two scientists noted that there were many more genes than chromosome pairs, thus setting the stage for the suggestion that some gene loci might be linked during meiotic processes. Who were these two scientists?

Answer: Walter Sutton and Theodor Boveri

29. What is the relationship between the degree of crossing over and the distance between two genes?

Answer: Direct because as the distance increases, the frequency of recombination increases.

30. When does crossing over occur?

Answer: At the four-strand stage of meiosis, after synapsis of homologous chromosomes and before the end of prophase I.

31. What is meant by the term second division segregation?

Answer: A condition that gives evidence of a crossover between a gene in question and the centromere: *aa++aa++* or *aa++++aa,* for example

Sample Questions: Chapter 8   Linkage and Chromosome Mapping in Eukaryotes

32. Describe a convenient method for determining gene order from three-point cross results.

Answer: Compare the double crossover class with the parental class and ask which gene has switched places. The gene that switched places is in the middle.

33.   Assume that a cross is made between an albino (*a*) strain of *Neurospora* and one that is normally pigmented (*A*). The frequency with which second division segregation occurs indicates that there are 25 map units between the *a* locus and the centromere. Given the four asci below, shade in the ascospore patterns with the appropriate frequency that would provide such a map distance (25 map units).

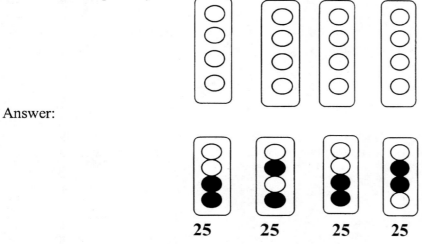

Answer:

34. Why is it possible to map the centromere in *Neurospora* and not in most other organisms?

Answer: Ascospores are held in order as meiotic products. This order is dependent on centromere migration, and a comparison of ascospore patterns enables one to determine whether crossovers have occurred. Quantifying such crossovers allows one to estimate map distance between the gene in question and the centromere.

35. Which is more frequent, meiotic or mitotic crossing over?

Answer: Meiotic crossing over is more frequent.

Sample Questions: *Chapter 8 Linkage and Chromosome Mapping in Eukaryotes*

True/False Format

36. Mendel predicted that some genes will be carried in the same chromosome.

Answer: False

37. The cross *GE/ge* X *ge/ge* produces the following progeny: *GE/ge* 404; *ge/ge* 396; *gE/ge* 97; *Ge/ge* 103. From these data one can conclude that the *G* and *E* loci assort independently.

Answer: False

38. The cross *GE/ge* X *ge/ge* produces the following progeny: *GE/ge* 404; *ge/ge* 396; *gE/ge* 97; *Ge/ge* 103. From these data one can conclude that the recombinant progeny are *gE/ge* and *Ge/ge*.

Answer: True

39. The cross *GE/ge* X *ge/ge* produces the following progeny: *GE/ge* 404; *ge/ge* 396; *gE/ge* 97; *Ge/ge* 103. From these data one can conclude that there are 20 map units between the *G* and *E* loci.

Answer: True

40. Linkage (viewed from results of typical crosses) always occurs when two loci are on the same chromosome.

Answer: False

41. Positive interference occurs when a crossover in one region of a chromosome interferes with crossovers in nearby regions.

Answer: True

42. In *Drosophila*, the frequency of crossing over is inversely proportional to the distance between two markers.

Answer: False

43. If two gene loci are on nonhomologous chromosomes, genes at these loci are expected to assort independently.

Answer: True

Sample Questions: Chapter 9 Mapping in Bacteria and Bacteriophages

Chapter 9

Multiple Choice Format

1. Name two forms of recombination in bacteria.

     A.   lytic and lysogenic
     B.   auxotrophic and prototrophic
     C.   conjugation and transduction
     D.   mixed and generalized
     E.   insertion and replication

Answer: C

2. Bacteriophage engage in two interactive cycles with bacteria. What are these cycles?

     A.   lytic and lysogenic
     B.   insertion and replication
     C.   auxotrophic and prototrophic
     D.   heteroduplex and homoduplex
     E.   negative and positive

Answer: A

3. A bacteriophage that is capable of entering either a lytic or a lysogenic cycle is called a(an)

     A.   temperate bacteriophage.
     B.   virulent bacteriophage.
     C.   plasmid.
     D.   episome.
     E.   plaque forming unit.

Answer: A

4. Transduction is a form of recombination in bacteria that involves

     A.   5-bromouracil.
     B.   F plasmids.
     C.   bacteriophage.
     D.   fertility factors.
     E.   physical contact between the bacteria involved.

Answer: C

5. The clearing made by bacteriophage in a lawn of bacteria on an agar plate is called a

      A.   clear zone.
      B.   lysogenic zone.
      C.   prophage.
      D.   plaque.
      E.   host range.

Answer: D

6. Name the general category into which double-stranded circular extrachromosomal DNA elements such as F factors, ColE1, and *R* would fall.

      A.   capsid
      B.   r-determinant
      C.   plaque
      D.   partial diploid
      E.   plasmid

Answer: E

7. Phage that are capable of undergoing either a lytic or a lysogenic cycle would be called

      A.   temperate.
      B.   virulent.
      C.   prophage.
      D.   plaque formers.
      E.   complementing.

Answer: A

Short Answer Format

8. Lysogeny is an important phenomenon in bacteria and phages. Briefly describe lysogeny (using labeled diagrams if helpful).

Answer: Lysogeny is the process in which a temperate bacteriophage infects a bacterial cell and subsequently integrates its chromosome into the bacterial chromosome.

Sample Questions: Chapter 9 Mapping in Bacteria and Bacteriophages

9. Compare and contrast bacteriophage lysis and lysogeny.

Answer: Both lysis and lysogeny involve bacterial/phage interactions related to the production of phage progeny. Lysis occurs when progeny phage burst from the bacterial cell, while lysogeny involves the incorporation of the phage chromosome into the bacterial chromosome.

10. Jacob, Wollman, and others developed a linkage map of *E. coli* based on time. What form of recombination is involved in generating a linkage map based on time?

Answer: An Hfr bacterium conjugating with an F⁻ strain allows one to generate a map which is dependent on the passage of the donor chromosome across a conjugation tube.

11. Assume the gene *trp*A in an auxotrophic strain of *E. coli* is located at 27 minutes, while the gene *pyr*E is located at 81 minutes.

(a) How are minutes arrived at in this context?

(b) Present an experimental scheme that would enable you to convert one of the auxotrophic strains to a prototrophic strain.

Answer:

(a) Minutes are arrived at by a Hfr X F⁻ matings.

(b) Hfr (wild type) X F⁻ (auxotroph)

12. Destinguish between F⁺ and F⁻ bacteria.

Answer: F+ bacteria contain an F factor or plasmid which is capable of initiating conjugation.

13. What is the role of the *rec*A gene in bacterial recombination?

Answer: The wildtype product of *rec*A is required for bacterial recombination to occur at an appreciable level. Absence of the RecA protein diminishes recombination by about 1000-fold.

14. How does and auxotroph differ from a prototroph?

Answer: Auxotrophs have lost, through mutation, the ability to grow on minimal medium.

15. Bacteriophage that can not undergo lysogeny but can infect bacteria are called_____.

Answer: virulent

16. Name the term used to describe the phenomenon in which a bacteriophage genome incorporates its genome into the chromosome of the host.

Answer: lysogeny

17. When a bacteriophage genome incorporates itself into the chromosome of the host, that phage genome is referred to as _____.

Answer: a prophage

18. What is a form of recombination in bacteria which involves the F plasmid?

Answer: conjugation

19. What are prototrophs?

Answer: Prototrophs are bacteria that can grow on minimal medium and are assumed to be wild type.

20. What is the role of the F factor in bacterial recombination?

Answer: The F factor functions in conjugation by generating the Hfr and F' recombinant possibilities.

21. What are the roles of the *rec*BCD genes?

Answer: They function in bacterial recombinaiton.

22. Present general structural features of a plasmid and give an example.

Answer: circular double-stranded DNA existing autonomously in the bacterial cytoplasm; F factor

23. What observations enabled researchers to determine that genes were involved in the integration of foreign DNA into the bacterial chromosome?

Answer: mutations allowed the identification of *rec* genes

24. In general, what two methods are used to grow bacteria in the laboratory?

Answer: liquid and semisolid (agar) media

Sample Questions: Chapter 9 Mapping in Bacteria and Bacteriophages

25. Name three forms of recombination in bacteria.

Answer: conjugation, transformation, transduction

26. Name the typical phases of the bacterial growth cycle in liquid culture medium.

Answer: lag, log (exponential), stationary

27. What is a significant difference between a lytic and lysogenic cycle?

Answer: In a lysogenic cycle, the phage genome does not insert into the bacterial chromosome.

28. If two different auxotrophic strains are placed in a liquid medium culture tube, prototrophic strains can sometimes be subsequently recovered. How is this possible?

Answer: reverse mutation, genetic suppression, genetic recombination (conjugation, transformation, conjugation)

29. Describe how different strains of *E.coli* can reveal different linkage arrangements of genes in Hfr crosses.

Answer: Different strains may have different F factors, and therefore different initiation points for chromosome transfer.

30. Bacteria that are in a particular physiological state to become transformed are called
_____.

Answer: competent

31. Explain what is meant by the term *heteroduplex* in a context of bacterial transformation.

Answer: If transforming DNA is derived from a genetically distinct bacterium, incoming DNA may be different from the host DNA. During initial stages of integration into the bacterial chromosome, the recombinant region contains one DNA that may have a different base sequence than the other strand. Because these strands are not genetically identical (complementary), this double stranded region is called a heteroduplex.

32. Assume that one counted 67 plaques on a bacterial plate from a 10^{-5} dilution of phage and 0.1 ml of the diluted phage was added to bacterial culture. What is the initial concentration of phage?

Answer: $67 \times 10^5 \times 10 = 6.7 \times 10^7$ pfu/ml (pfu = plaque forming units)

Sample Questions: Chapter 9 Mapping in Bacteria and Bacteriophages

33. A form of bacterial recombination that involves a viral intermediate is called _____.

Answer: transduction

34. What is a bacteriophage?

Answer: A bacteriophage is a virus that has a bacterium as its host.

35. What is meant by the term *cotransformation*?

Answer: Cotransformation occurs when several linked genes are transformed simultaneously.

True/False Format

36. In a bacterial cross where the donor (Hfr) is a^+b^+ and the recipient strain (F⁻) is a^-b^-, it is expected that recombinant bacteria will all be a^+b^+.

Answer: False

37.   An Hfr cell can initiate chromosome transfer from one *E.coli* to another.

Answer: True

38. To produce recombinants in bacteria, one crossover is better than two.

Answer: False

39. R plasmids often contain genes for antibody production.

Answer: False

40. A plaque is a substance that causes mutation in bacteria.

Answer: False

Sample Questions: Chapter 9 Mapping in Bacteria and Bacteriophages

41. Cotransduction of genes is an indication that the genes are linked.

Answer: True

42. Lysogeny is a process thatoccurs during transformation and conjugation.

Answer: False

43. Viral mutations and variants are often categorized by changes in host range and/or plaque morphology.

Answer: True

44. A symbiotic relationship between a phage and a bacterium apparently occurs in the process of lysogeny.

Answer: True

45. Lysogeny is most likely associated with transduction.

Answer: True

46. The interrupted mating technique provides for a genetic map in *Drosophila*.

Answer: False

Chapter 10

Multiple Choice Format

1. The basic structure of a nucleotide includes the following components:

      A.   amino acids
      B.   tryptophan and leucine
      C.   base, sugar, and phosphate
      D.   mRNA, rRNA, and tRNA
      E.   phosphorus and sulfur

Answer: C

2. The classic Hershey and Chase (1952) experiment that provided evidence in support of DNA as the genetic material in bacteriophage made use of the following labeled components:

      A.   phosphorus and sulfur
      B.   nitrogen and oxygen
      C.   tritium
      D.   hydrogen
      E.   none of the above

Answer: A

3. Hershey and Chase (1952) used differential labeling to determine that _____ is the genetic material in _____.

      A.   DNA, bacteriophage
      B.   RNA, eukaryotes
      C.   DNA, eukaryotes
      D.   RNA, yeast
      E.   DNA, yeast

Answer: A

Sample Questions: Chapter 10 DNA Structure and Analysis

4. What are the two major components of the tobacco mosaic virus?

      A.   RNA and DNA
      B.   DNA and protein
      C.   RNA and protein
      D.   lipids and nucleic acids
      E.   carbohydrates and nucleic acids

Answer: C

5. Considering the structure of double-stranded DNA, what kinds of bonds hold one complementary strand to the other?

      A.   ionic
      B.   covalent
      C.   Van der Waals
      D.   hydrogen
      E.   hydrophobic and hydrophilic

Answer: D

6. Regarding the structure of DNA, the covalently arranged combination of a deoxyribose and nitrogenous base is called a

      A.   nucleotide.
      B.   ribonucleotide.
      C.   monophospate nucleoside.
      D.   oligonucleotide.
      E.   nucleoside.

Answer: E

Short Answer Format

7. Briefly describe the relationship between the phenomenon of transformation and the discovery that DNA is the genetic material in bacteria.

Answer: Transformation is the process whereby one organism is genetically altered by exposure to DNA from another organism.   Since DNA can carry heritable traits from one organism to another, it must be the genetic material.

Sample Questions: Chapter 10 DNA Structure and Analysis

8. Which of the following clusters of terms accurately describes DNA as it is generally viewed to exist in prokaryotes and eukaryotes?

        A.   double-stranded, parallel, (A+T)/C+G) = variable, (A+G)/(C+T)= 1.0
        B.   double-stranded, antiparallel, (A+T)/C+G) = variable, (A+G)/(C+T) = 1.0
        C.   single-stranded, antiparallel, (A+T)/C+G) = 1.0, (A+G)/(C+T) = 1.0
        D.   double-stranded, parallel, (A+T)/C+G) = 1.0, (A+G)/(C+T) = 1.0
        E.   double-stranded, antiparallel, (A+T)/C+G) = variable, (A+G)/(C+T) = variable

Answer: B

9. Present an overview of two classical experiments demonstrating that DNA is the genetic material. Can RNA be the genetic material? Explain.

Answer: (1) Transformation in bacteria (Griffith through Avery, *et al.*); see appropriate figures in the Klug/Cummings text. (2) The Hershey and Chase experiment in bacteriophage; see appropriate figures in the Klug/Cummings text. Yes, RNA can be the genetic material as described for the tobacco mosaic virus (TMV), retroviruses, and many others.

10.   Describe four major functions of DNA in a cell.

Answer: *Replication* = duplication of genetic material. *Expression* = production of a phenotype. *Storage* = stable maintenance and passage of information. *Variation* = capacity for alteration.

11.   Consider the structure of double-stranded DNA.   When DNA is placed into distilled water it denatures; however, by adding NaCl, the DNA renatures. Why?

Answer: The negatively charged phosphates repel each other on the two sides of the helix. In distilled water, these charges are not neutralized (by positively charged ions), and the hydrogen bonds holding the double helix together are broken.

12.   If the GC content of a DNA molecule is 60%, what are the molar percentages of the four bases (G, C, T, A)?

Answer: G = 30%, C = 30%, A = 20%, T = 20%.

13. Explain how and why the following circumstances influence characteristics of temperature-induced DNA melting.

        Percentage of GC base pairs
        Urea (forms hydrogen bonds with bases)
        Sodium chloride (neutralizes negatively charged phosphates)

Sample Questions: Chapter 10 DNA Structure and Analysis

Answer: GC pairs are composed of three hydrogen bonds and require more energy (heat) to separate than AT pairs. Urea competes for hydrogen bonds, so the bases pair with the urea rather than with each other. This weakens the complementary associations required to hold the DNA helix together, so less heat is required for melting. The sodium of sodium chloride associates with and neutralizes the strong negative charges on the phosphates. The phosphates don't repel each other with the sodium ion present; thus, the double-stranded structure requires more energy to melt.

14. Assume that the molar percentage of thymine in a double-stranded DNA is 20. What are the percentages of the four bases (G, C, T, A)? If the DNA is single-stranded, would you change your answer?

Answer: G = 30%, C = 30%, A = 20%, T = 20%. Yes, more than likely.

15. (a) Assume that A + T/G + C equals 0.5 in one strand of DNA. What is the ratio of these bases in the complementary strand? (b) If A + G/T + C equals 0.5 in one strand, what is the ratio of these bases in the complementary strand?

Answer: (a) 0.5 (b) 2.0

16. The base content of a sample of DNA is as follows: A = 31%, G = 31%, T = 19%, C = 19%. What conclusion can be drawn from this information?

Answer: The sample of DNA is single-stranded.

17. Double-stranded nucleic acids are said to be antiparallel. What structural configuration is antiparallel?

Answer: The C-5' to C-3' orientations run in opposite directions.

18. List three forms of DNA.

Answer: A-DNA, B-DNA, Z-DNA

19. Considering the Central Dogma of Molecular Biology, what three general properties are ascribed to DNA?

Answer: storage and expression of information, variation through mutation

20. At what approximate wavelengths do DNA, RNA, and proteins absorb light?

Answer: 260 nm, 260 nm, and 280 nm, respectively

Sample Questions: Chapter 10 DNA Structure and Analysis

21. The Avery, et al. (1944) contribution to an understanding of molecular biology was_____.

Answer: a demonstration that DNA is the genetic material in *Diplococci*

22. All other factors being equal, the renaturation of complementary nucleic acid sequences occurs in what order, from fastest to slowest?

Answer: highly repetitive, moderately repetitive, unique sequences

23. List two major differences between RNA and DNA at the level of the nucleotide.

Answer: ribose in RNA, deoxyribose in DNA, uracil in RNA replaces thymine in DNA

24. Provide an overview of the structure of Z-DNA.

Answer: Z-DNA is a left-handed helix with two antiparallel complementary strands, 1.8 nm in diameter, 12 bases per turn, having a zigzag configuration and a shallow major groove.

25. In the 1860s, a Swiss chemist, Friedrick Miescher, isolated an acidic substance from cell nuclei. What was the name of this substance, and what was its significance?

Answer: nuclein; contains DNA

26. Experiments conducted in the 1920s by Frederick Griffith involving the bacterium *Diplococcus pneumoniae* demonstrated that a substance from one bacterial strain could genetically transform other bacterial strains. What was the name of the substance capable of such transformation, and who finally determined its identity?

Answer: deoxyribonucleic acid; Avery, et al. (1944)

27. The strongest direct evidence that DNA is the genetic material comes from what contemporary methodology?

Answer: recombinant DNA technology

28. Beatrice Mintz and others microinjected DNA into a fertilized mouse egg, which, after reaching maturity, could be transmitted to the mouse's offspring. What is the general term used to describe an organism that incorporates foreign DNA?

Answer: transgenic

29. Name the pyrimidines and purines in DNA.

Answer: pyrimidines: cytosine and thymine; purines: adenine and guanine

Sample Questions: Chapter 10 DNA Structure and Analysis

30. What is the name of the precursor molecule used in nucleic acid synthesis?

Answer: triphosphonucleoside

31. During the polymerization of nucleic acids, covalent bonds are formed between neighboring nucleotides. Which carbons are involved in such bonds?

Answer: C-3' and C-5'

32. What is the difference between a polynucleotide and an oligonucleotide?

Answer: Polynucleotides are polymers longer than 20 nucleotides, while oligonucleotides are shorter than polynucleotides.

33. Is the figure to the right DNA or RNA?
   Is the circle closest to the 5' or 3' end?

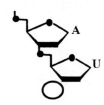

Answer: RNA, 3'

34. Is the figure to the right DNA or RNA?
   Is the circle closest to the 5' or 3' end?

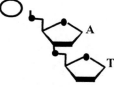

Answer: DNA, 5'

35. Suppose that the dinucleotide to the right was cleaved with the enzyme spleen diesterase, which breaks the covalent bond connecting the phosphate to C-5'. After such cleavage, to which nucleoside is the phosphate now attached?

Answer: deoxyadenosine

36. What is meant by the term *antiparallel*?

Answer: The two chains in a double stranded nucleic acid are connected in opposite directions in terms of 5'-3' orientations.

37. When and in which journal did Watson and Crick publish their now-famous paper entitled "Molecular Structure of Nucleic Acids: A Structure for Deoxyribose Nucleic Acid"?

Answer: 1953, *Nature*

Sample Questions: *Chapter 10 DNA Structure and Analysis*

True/False Format

38. In ribose, the 2' C has an OH attached to it.

Answer: True

39. DNA has no sulfur and proteins have no phosphorous.

Answer: True

40. The transforming principle discovered by Griffith is RNA.

Answer: False

41. G and C are present in both DNA and RNA.

Answer: True

42. Hershey and Chase used labeled DNA and protein to determine that DNA is the genetic material in bacteria.

Answer: False

43. Avery, et al. (1944) determined that DNA is the genetic material in the T2 bacteriophage.

Answer: False

44. In 1953, Watson and Crick published a paper that described the structure of DNA.

Answer: True

45. Deoxyribonuclease is an enzyme that adds 3'-hydroxyl groups to RNA.

Answer: False

46. When considering the structure of DNA, we would say that complementary strands are antiparallel.

Answer: True

47. A retrovirus is capable of making DNA from an RNA template.

Answer: True

Chapter 11

Multiple Choice Format

1. Which of the following terms accurately describes the replication of DNA *in vivo*?

      A.   conservative
      B.   dispersive
      C.   semi-discontinuous
      D.   nonlinear
      E.   nonreciprocal

Answer: C

2. In *E. coli*, which terms accurately reflect the nature of replication of the chromosome?

      A.   bidirectional and fixed point of initiation
      B.   unidirectional and reciprocal
      C.   unidirectional and fixed point of initiation
      D.   multirepliconic
      E.   bidirectional and multirepliconic

Answer: A

3. DNA polymerase III adds nucleotides

      A.   to the 3' end of the RNA primer.
      B.   to the 5' end of the RNA primer.
      C.   in the place of the primer RNA after it is removed.
      D.   to both ends of the RNA primer.
      E.   to internal sites in the DNA template.

Answer: A

Sample Questions: Chapter 11 DNA Replication and Synthesis

4. DNA polymerase I is thought to add nucleotides

  A.   to the 5' end of the primer.
  B.   to the 3' end of the primer.
  C.   in the place of the primer RNA after it is removed.
  D.   on single-stranded templates without need for an RNA primer.
  E.   in a 5' to 5' direction.

Answer: C

5. Structures located at the ends of eukaryotic chromosomes are called

  A.   centromeres.
  B.   telomerases.
  C.   recessive mutations.
  D.   telomeres.
  E.   permissive mutations.

Answer: D

6. Which set of terms accurately reflects the nature of DNA replication in prokaryotes?

  A.   fixed point of initiation, bidirectional, conservative
  B.   fixed point of initiation, unidirectional, conservative
  C.   random point of initiation, bidirectional, semiconservative
  D.   fixed point of initiation, bidirectional, semiconservative
  E.   random point of initiation, unidirectional, semiconservative

Answer: D

7. The discontinuous aspect of replication of DNA *in vivo* is caused by

  A.   polymerase slippage.
  B.   trinucleotide repeats.
  C.   the 5' to 3' polarity restriction.
  D.   topoisomerases cutting the DNA in a random fashion.
  E.   sister chromatid exchanges.

Answer: C

Sample Questions: Chapter 11 DNA Replication and Synthesis

Short Answer Format

8.   Assume that a strain of *E. coli* is grown for many generations in ^{15}N (present in the ammonium ion), a heavy isotope of nitrogen (^{14}N). Under this condition, assume that the DNA has a density of 1.723 gm/cm^3 (with water being 1.00 gm/cm^3). Assume that DNA containing only ^{14}N has a density of 1.700.   Bacteria from the ^{15}N culture were washed in buffer and transferred to ^{14}N medium for one generation. DNA was extracted.

(a) What would be the expected density of the extracted DNA ?

(b) Assuming that the extracted DNA was completely denatured (heat at 90° C for 15 minutes), what would be the density (or densities) of the DNA (or DNAs) in the heated extract? Explain your answer. (Note: Assume that DNA has the same density whether single- or double-stranded, which is not actually the case.)

(c) Assuming that the molar percentage of adenine in the extracted DNA was 20%, what would be the expected molar percentages of the other nitrogenous bases in this DNA?

(d) Assume that a fraction of the extracted DNA was digested to completion with the enzyme snake venom diesterase. This enzyme cleaves between the phosphate and the 3' carbon. Present a "simplified" diagram illustrating the structure of the predominant resulting molecule.

Answers: (a)   approximately 1.712

               (b)   1.723 and 1.700

               (c)   thymine = 20%, guanine = 30%, cytosine = 30%

               (d)

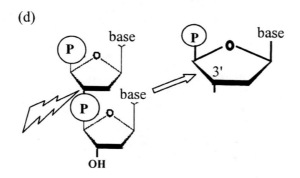

Sample Questions: Chapter 11 DNA Replication and Synthesis

9. The diagram below of a generalized tetranucleotide will serve as a basis for the five questions marked "a" through "e."

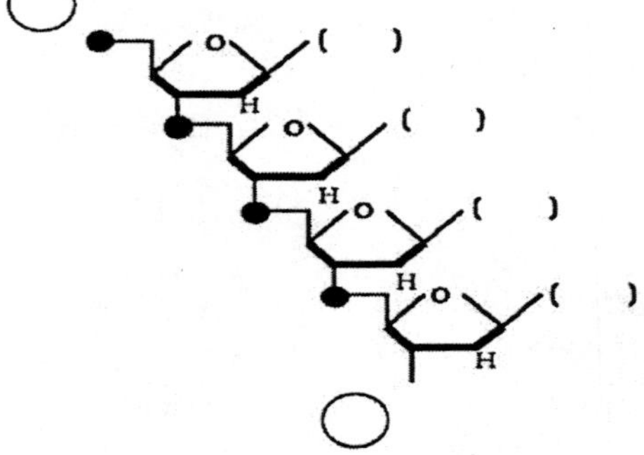

(a) Is this a DNA or an RNA molecule?

(b) Place an X (in one of the circles provided) at the 3' end of this tetranucleotide.

(c) Given that the DNA strand servomg as a template for the synthesis of this tetranucleotide was composed of the bases 5'- A C A G - 3', fill in the parentheses (in the diagram) with the expected bases.

(d) Suppose that one of the precursors for this tetranucleotide (in the diagram) was a ^{32}P-labeled guanine nucleoside triphosphate (the innermost phosphate containing the radioactive phosphorus). Circle the radioactive phosphorus atom as it exists in the tetranucleotide.

(e) Given that spleen diesterase (breaks between the phosphate and the 5' carbon) digests the pictured tetranucleotide, state which base(s) among the breakdown products will be expected to be attached to the ^{32}P.

Answers:

    (a)   DNA
    (b)   place in bottom circle
    (c)   3'-TGTC-5'
    (d)   phosphate on the 5' side of the guanine
    (e)   thymine

Sample Questions: Chapter 11 DNA Replication and Synthesis

10. Assume that you are microscopically examining mitotic metaphase cells of an organism with a 2n chromosome number of 4 (one pair metacentric and one pair telocentric). Assume also that the cell passed through one S phase labeling (innermost phosphate of dTTP radioactive) just prior to the period of observation. Assuming that the circle represents a cell, draw its chromosomes and the autoradiographic pattern you would expect to see.

Answer:

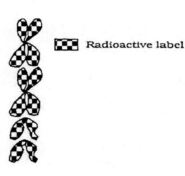

Radioactive label

11. The Meselson and Stahl experiment provided conclusive evidence for the semiconservative replication of DNA in *E. coli*. What pattern of bands would occur in a CsCl gradient for conservative replication?

Answer: After one generation in the ^{14}N, there would be two bands, one heavy and one light (no intermediate). After the second generation in the ^{14}N , there would also be two bands, one heavy and one light (no intermediate).

12. Given that the nature of DNA replication in eukaryotes is not as well understood as in prokaryotes, (a) present a description of DNA (chromosome) replication as presently viewed in eukaryotes and (b) state known differences between prokaryotic and eukaryotic DNA replication.

Answer:

(a) Eukaryotic DNA is replicated in a manner very similar to that in *E. coli*: bidirectional, continuous on one strand and discontinuous on the other, similar requirements for synthesis (four deoxyribonucleoside triphosphates, divalent cation, template, and primer).

(b) Okazaki fragments are about one-tenth the size of those in bacteria. Different portions of the chromosome (euchromatin, heterochromatin) replicate at different times. There are multiple replication origins in eukaryotic chromosomes.

Sample Questions: Chapter 11 DNA Replication and Synthesis

13. Below is a list of terms, each term relating to the replication of chromosomes. Describe the role (relationship) of each in (to) chromosome replication.

Okazaki fragment
lagging strand
bidirectional

Answer: Okazaki fragment: short single-stranded stretches of DNA on the lagging strand. See figures in the Klug/Cummings text.

Lagging strand: that side of the replication fork where synthesis is discontinuous. See figures in the Klug/Cummings text.

Bidirectional: from the point of initiation, replication occurs in both directions along the DNA. See figures in the Klug/Cummings text.

14. Assume that you were growing cells in culture and had determined the cell cycle time to be 24 hours. You introduce ^{3}H thymidine and prepare autoradiographs of metaphase chromosomes after 48 hours. Of the chromosomes that are labeled, you expect two classes: one class that had completed one S phase in the label, and a second class that had completed a cellular division and an additional S phase in the label. Draw the DNA (double-stranded) labeling pattern for each chromosome (drawn below) you would expect to find in these two types of metaphase chromosomes. (Use a broken line {- - -} for labeled single strands of DNA and a solid line for unlabeled single strands of DNA.)

(a) A metaphase chromosome having replicated once in label:

(b) A metaphase chromosome having "gone through two S phases in label":

Answer:

(a)

(b)

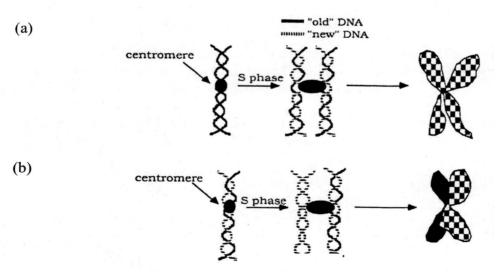

Sample Questions: Chapter 11 DNA Replication and Synthesis

15. Below is a diagram of DNA replication as currently believed to occur in *E. coli*. From specific points, arrows lead to numbers.   Answer the questions below relating to the locations specified by the numbers.

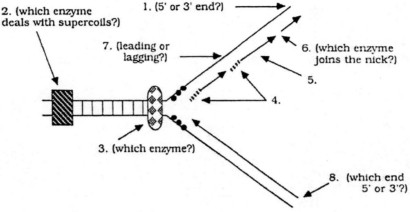

(1) What end (5' or 3') of the molecule is here?

(2) What enzyme is probably functioning here to deal with supercoils in the DNA?

(3) What enzyme is probably functioning here to unwind the DNA?

(4) What nucleic acid is probably depicted here?

(5) What are these short DNA fragments usually called?

(6) What enzyme probably functions here to couple these two newly synthesized fragments of DNA?

(7)   Is this strand the leading or lagging strand?

(8) What end (5' or 3') of the molecule is here?

Answer:

    (1) 5'
    (2) gyrase
    (3) helicase
    (4) RNA
    (5) Okazaki fragments
    (6) ligase
    (7) lagging
    (8) 5'

Sample Questions: Chapter 11 DNA Replication and Synthesis

16. Assume that you grew a culture of *E. coli* for many generations in medium containing ^{15}N (from the ammonium ion), a heavy isotope of nitrogen. You extract DNA from a portion of the culture and determine its density to be 1.723 gm/cm^3 (call this sample A). You then wash the remaining *E. coli* cells and grow them for one generation in ^{14}N, extract the DNA from a portion of the culture, and determine its density to be 1.715 gm/cm^3 (call this sample B). You let the culture grow for one more generation in ^{14}N, and extract the DNA (call this sample C). Each sample of DNA (A, B, and C) is then heated to completely denature the double-stranded structures, cooled quickly (to keep the strands separate), and subjected to ultracentrifugation. Present the centrifugation profiles for heat-denatured DNA (samples A, B, and C) you would expect. Use the graph below. (Note: Although not the case, assume that single-stranded DNA has the same density as double-stranded DNA.)

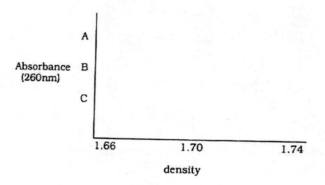

Answer:

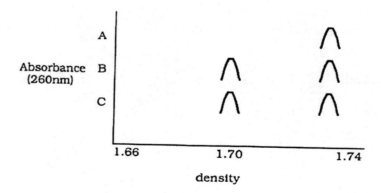

Sample Questions: Chapter 11 DNA Replication and Synthesis

17. Assume that you grew a culture of *E. coli* for many generations in medium containing ^{15}N (from the ammonium ion), a heavy isotope of nitrogen. You extract DNA from a portion of the culture and determine its density to be 1.723 gm/cm^3 (call this sample A). You then wash the remaining *E. coli* cells and grow them for one generation in ^{14}N, and extract the DNA from a portion of the culture (call this sample B). You let the culture grow for one more generation in ^{14}N, and extract the DNA (call this sample C). Each sample of DNA (A, B, and C) is then subjected to ultracentrifugation. Present the centrifugation profiles you would expect under (a) semiconservative replication, and (b) conservative replication. Use the graphs below. (Note: Assume that unlabeled (^{14}N) DNA has a density of 1.700 gm/cm^3.)

Answer:

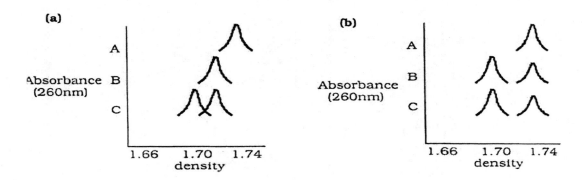

18. List four enzymes known to be involved in the replication of DNA in bacteria.

Answer: DNA polymerase I, III, ligase, RNA primase, helicase, gyrase

19. What structural circumstance in DNA sets up the requirement for its semidiscontinuous nature of replication?

Answer: 5' to 3' polarity restrictions of DNA synthesis and the antiparallel orientation of the DNA strands in DNA

20. As unwinding of the helix occurs during DNA replication, tension is created ahead of the replication fork. Describe the nature of this tension, and state the manner in which the tension is resolved.

Answer: supercoiling, DNA gyrase

21. The complex of proteins involved in the replication of DNA is called what?

Answer: replisome

Sample Questions: Chapter 11 DNA Replication and Synthesis

22. Given that the origin of replication is fixed in *E. coli*, what signals the location of the origin?

Answer: a region called *ori*C, which consists of about 250 base pairs characterized by repeating sequences of 9 and 13 bases (9mers and 13mers)

23. What protein is responsible for the initial step in unwinding the DNA helix during replication?

Answer: *Dna*A

24. During DNA replication, what is the function of RNA primase?

Answer: RNA primase provides a free 3'-OH upon which DNA polymerization depends.

25. Describe the rate of DNA replication in prokaryotes and eukaryotes.

Answer: In *E. coli*, approximately 100 kb are added per minute, while in eukaryotes only 0.5 to 5 kb are added per minute.

26. Describe the replication unit in prokaryotes and eukaryotes.

Answer: one replicon in prokaryotes, multiple replicons in eukaryotes

27. Describe the DNA base sequence arrangement at the end of the *Tetrahymena* chromosome and the resolution of DNA replication at the end of a linear DNA strand.

Answer: Telomeres terminate in a 5'-TTGGGG-3' sequence, and telomerase is capable of adding repeats to the ends, thus allowing the completion of replication without leaving a gap and shortening the chromosome following each replication.

28. Describe a somewhat extraordinary finding related to the *Tetrahymena telomerase* enzyme.

Answer: The enzyme contains a short piece of RNA that is essential for its catalytic activity.

29. What term is used to describe genetic exchange at equivalent positions along two chromosomes with substantial DNA sequence homology?

Answer: general or homologous recombination

30. Describe the function of the RecA protein.

Answer: It promotes the exchange of reciprocal single-stranded DNA molecules by enhancing hydrogen bond formation during strand displacement.

Sample Questions: Chapter 11 DNA Replication and Synthesis

31. What three models were suggested to originally describe the nature of DNA replication?

Answer: conservative, semiconservative, dispersive

32. Given the diagram below, assume that a G1 chromosome (left) underwent one round of replication in ^{3}H-thymidine and the metaphase chromosome (right) had both chromatids labeled. Which of the following replicative models (*conservative, dispersive, semiconservative*) could be eliminated by this observation?

Answer: conservative

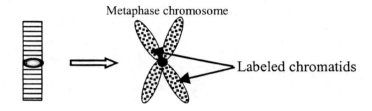

33. Meselson and Stahl determined that DNA replication in *E.coli* is semiconservative. What additive did they initially supply to the medium in order to distinguish "new" from "old" DNA?

Answer: ^{15}N

34. Briefly describe what is meant by the term *autoradiography* and identify a classic experiment that used autoradiography to determine the replicative nature of DNA in eukaryotes.

Answer: Autoradiography is a technique that allows an isotope to be localized within a cell; Taylor, Woods, and Hughes (1957) experiment using ^{3}H-thymidine.

35. What primary ingredients, coupled with DNA polymerase I, are needed for the *in vitro* synthesis of DNA?

Answer: dNTP, DNA template, primer DNA or RNA, Mg^{++} (appropriate buffering, temperature, salt concentrations might be considered "secondary" ingredients)

36. DNA replication *in vivo* requires a primer with a free 3' end. What molecular species provides this 3' end, and how is it provided?

Answer: The free 3' end is provided by an RNA primer, which is provided by the enzymatic activity of RNA primase.

Sample Questions: Chapter 11 DNA Replication and Synthesis

True/False Format

37. DNA replication occurs in the 5' to 3' direction; that is, new nucleoside triphosphates are added to the 3' end.

Answer: True

38. DNA replicates conservatively, meaning, of the two daughter double-helices, one is "old" and the other is "new."

Answer: False

39. DNA strand replication begins with an RNA primer.

Answer: True

40. In general, DNA replicates semiconservatively and bidirectionally.

Answer: True

41. In ligase-deficient strains of *E. coli*, DNA and chromosomal replication is unaltered because ligase is not involved in DNA replication.

Answer: False

42. During replication, primase adds a DNA primer to RNA.

Answer: False

43. *Spleen phoshodiesterase* is an enzyme that adds nucleoside triphosphates to the 3' end of each growing DNA strand.

Answer: False

Sample Questions: Chapter 11 DNA Replication and Synthesis

44. The active form of DNA polymerase consists of two sets (a dimer) of 10 separate polypeptide subunits.

Answer: True

45. An endonuclease is involved in removing bases sequentially from one end of DNA or the other.

Answer: False

46. In the Meselson and Stahl (1958) experiment, bean plants (*Vicia faba*) were radioactively labeled so that autoradiographs could be made of chromosomes.

Answer: False

Chapter 12

Multiple Choice Format

1. Viral chromosomes exist in a variety of structures and are made up of the following:

      A.   protein and lipid coding sequences
      B.   DNA only
      C.   DNA and RNA
      D.   RNA only
      E.   DNA, RNA, and protein

Answer: C

2. In *E. coli*, the genetic material is composed of

      A.   circular, double-stranded DNA.
      B.   linear, double-stranded DNA.
      C.   RNA and protein.
      D.   circular, double-stranded RNA.
      E.   polypeptide chains.

Answer: A

3. Eukaryotic chromosomes contain two general domains that relate to the degree of condensation. These two regions are

      A.   called heterochromatin and euchromatin.
      B.   uniform in the genetic information they contain.
      C.   separated by large stretches of repetitive DNA.
      D.   each void of typical protein-coding sequences of DNA.
      E.   void of introns.

Answer: A

Sample Questions: Chapter 12 Chromosome Structure and DNA Sequence Organization

4. In human chromosomes, there are satellite DNA sequences of about 170 base pairs in length present in tandem arrays of up to 1 million base pairs. Found mainly in centromere regions, they are called

    A.   telomeres.
    B.   primers.
    C.   alphoid families.
    D.   euchromatic regions.
    E.   telomere-associated sequences.

Answer: C

5. In addition to highly repetitive and unique DNA sequences, a third category of DNA sequences exists. What is it called and what types of elements are involved?

    A.   composite DNA; telomeres and heterochromatin
    B.   dominant DNA; euchromatin and heterochromatin
    C.   multiple gene family DNA; hemoglobin and 5.0S RNA
    D.   moderately repetitive DNA; SINEs, LINEs, and VNTRs
    E.   permissive DNA; centromeres and heterochromatin

Answer: D

6. Chromatin of eukaryotes is organized into repeating interactions with protein octomers called nucleosomes. Nucleosomes are composed of which class of molecules?

    A.   histones
    B.   glycoproteins
    C.   lipids
    D.   H1 histones
    E.   nonhistone chromosomal proteins

Answer: A

Sample Questions: Chapter 12 Chromosome Structure and DNA Sequence Organization

7. The fact that some organisms contain much larger amounts of DNA than apparently "needed" and that some relatively closely related organisms may have vastly different amounts of DNA is more typical in
     A.   viruses than in bacteria.
     B.   RNA viruses than in DNA viruses.
     C.   eukaryotes than in prokaryotes.
     D.   the family "alphoid" rather than the diphloid family.
     E.   prokaryotes than in eukaryotes.

Answer: C

Short Answer Format

8. While mutations have been observed in many different genes, they have not been isolated in histones. Why does this seem reasonable? If one wanted to produce antibodies to histones, would it be an easy task? Explain your answer.

Answer: Histones represent one of the most conserved molecules in nature because they are involved in a fundamental and important function relating to chromosome structure. Mutations are probably lethal. Since all antibody-producing organisms have essentially the same histones, it would be difficult to find an organism to produce histone antibodies, for to do so would be self-destructive.

9. What is unusual about the amino acid composition of histones? How is the function of histones related to the amino acid composition? Of which histones are nucleosomes composed?

Answer: Histones contain large amounts of positively charged amino acids, such as lysine and arginine. Thus, they can bind electrostatically to the negatively charged phosphate groups of nucleotides. Nucleosomes are composed of all histones except H1.

10. Describe the basic structure of a nucleosome. What is the role of histone H1?

Answer: Nucleosomes are composed of four different histone molecules, each of which exists twice, thus forming an octomer. Histone H1 is between nucleosomes.

11. Compare and contrast the genetic map with the cytological map produced by studying altered banding patterns in *Drosophila*.

Answer: Both produce a map with the same order of genes; however, the relative distance between loci differs considerably in many cases. In other words, the distribution of crossing over along a chromosome is not uniform.

Sample Questions: Chapter 12   Chromosome Structure and DNA Sequence Organization

12. Compare and contrast the chromosome structure of viruses, bacteria, and eukaryotes.

Answer: The amount of DNA per structure (virus particle, bacterium, cell) increases as one goes from viruses to eukaryotic cells. Viral chromosomes may be composed of single-stranded or double-stranded RNA or DNA while bacterial and eukaryotic DNA is double-stranded. Bacterial DNA is considered to be a covalently closed circle, while the "global" structure of eukaryotic chromosomes is uncertain. While some proteins are associated with viral and bacterial DNA, the regularly spaced histones of eukaryotic chromosomes are unique.

13. A particular variant of the lambda bacteriophage has a DNA double-stranded genome of 51,365 base pairs. How long would this DNA be?

Answer: One base pair is 0.34 nm, therefore: 51,365 bp X 0.34nm/bp = 17,464nm or 17.46 μm.

14. List the components of a nucleosome.

Answer: Histones H2A, H2B, H3, and H4 exist as two types of tetramers: $(H2A)_2 + (H2B)_2$, and $(H3)_2 + (H4)_2$.

15. List several configurations that characterize viral chromosomes.

Answer: DNA (single- and double-stranded), RNA (single- and double-stranded), linear, circular

16. What is an intron, and what is the relationship between an intron and heterogeneous nuclear RNA (hnRNA)?

Answer: An intron is a section of DNA which when transcribed as part of an RNA is eventually spliced out of that RNA. The entire gene transcript that may serve as an eventual mRNA (after intron removal and other forms of processing) is called heterogeneous nuclear RNA.

17. What are minisatellites and microsatellites?

Answer: Both are highly repetitive, relatively short DNA sequences.

18. Describe the chromosomal conformations of ϕX174 and polyoma viruses.

Answer: single-stranded DNA, circular; double-stranded DNA, circular, respectively

Sample Questions: Chapter 12 Chromosome Structure and DNA Sequence Organization

19. What similarities do bacterial chromosomes and eukaryotic chromosomes share?

Answer: Both have double-stranded DNA and several types of proteins associated with that DNA (nucleosomes in eukaryotes and HU and H proteins in bacteria).

20. Discuss the possible origin of mitochondria and chloroplasts.

Answer: development of endosymbionic relationships from primitive, free-living bacteria-like organisms

21. Describe the method of replication of mtDNA.

Answer: The circular, double-stranded duplex is replicated semiconservatively.

22. List nuclear-encoded gene products that are essential to the biological activity of mitochondria.

Answer: DNA and RNA polymerases, initiation and elongation factors required for translation, ribosomal proteins, aminoacyl tRNA synthetases, and some RNAs

23. To which antibiotics are chloroplasts sensitive? Are bacteria also sensitive to these antibiotics?

Answer: chloramphenicol, erythromycin, streptomycin, spectinomycin; yes

24. What is the endosymbiont theory championed by Lynn Margulis?

Answer: Mitochondria and chloroplasts may have originated as distinct bacteria-like particles that became incorporated into primitive eukaryotic cells.

25. What are histones, and how are they arranged in nucleosomes?

Answer: Histones are represented by five main classes of relatively small basic proteins containing relatively large amounts of lysine and arginine. Nucleosomes are made of two each of four types of histones.

Sample Questions: Chapter 12   Chromosome Structure and DNA Sequence Organization

26. When native chromatin is digested with micrococcal nuclease, what significant result occurs?

Answer: DNA fragments of approximately 200 base pairs in length are formed.

27. Briefly state what is meant by repetitive DNA.

Answer: DNA is present in repeated sequences, such as $(GACAT)_n$.

28. What is meant by SINE in terms of chromosome structure? LINE? Why are they called "repetitive"?

Answer: Short Interspersed Elements, a moderately repetitive sequence class: Long Interspersed Elements. Multiple copies exist -- up to 900,000 *Alu* sequences, for example.

29. What are VNTRs, and how do they relate to DNA fingerprinting?

Answer: Variable Number Tandem Repeats of 15 to 100 base pairs long; they vary among individuals

30. Approximately how much of the genome is composed of repetitive DNA?

Answer: About 5-10 % of a mammalian genome is highly repetitive, while about 30 percent is moderately repetitive.

31. Briefly describe the makeup of VNTRs (variable number tandem repeats).

Answer: VNTRs are repeating DNA sequences of about 15 to 100 bases pairs long, found within and between genes. These sequences may be repeated to give regions 1000 to 5000 bp in length. They are dispersed throughout the genome.

32. What are chromosomal regions representing evolutionary vestiges of duplicated copies of genes that have underdone sufficient mutations to render them untranscribable called?

Answer: pseudogenes

33. In the formation of nucleosomes, one histone class, H1, is not directly involved, yet it does associate with DNA to form higher level chromosomal structures. Where does this histone (H1) associate?

Answer: in the spaces between nucleosome/DNA complexes

34. Until about 1970, mitotic chromosomes viewed under the microscope could be distinguished only by their size, positions of centromeres, and "satellites" in some cases. However, various staining techniques have revealed a different view of chromosomes because they allow the visualization of _____

Answer: bands similar to those of polytene chromosomes.

35. In humans, approximately how many base pairs are present in the haploid genome?

Answer: approximately 3.2×10^9

True/False Format

36. Certain structural and functional similarities exist among chloroplasts, mitochondria, and bacteria. Thus, they are considered to be in some way phylogenetically related.

Answer: True

37. *In situ* hybridization allows one to visualize the origin of labeled RNA or DNA in a tissue or cell.

Answer: True

38. Telomerase is an enzyme involved in the replication of the ends of eukaryotic chromosomes.

Answer: True

39. In contrast with euchromatin, heterochromatin contains more genes and is earlier replicating.

Answer: False

Sample Questions: Chapter 12 Chromosome Structure and DNA Sequence Organization

40. The *E. coli* chromosome is circular and double-stranded DNA.

Answer: True

41. Each human contains an identical set of VNTRs.

Answer: False

42. Viral genomes are always linear, double-stranded DNA.

Answer: False

43. An unfortunate circumstance of human chromosome methodology is that banding (natural or induced) is not possible.

Answer: False

44. Approximately 95% of the human genome is believed to contain functional genes.

Answer: False

45. The human genome contains approximately 3000 times the number of genes as a sea urchin.

Answer: False

46. In humans, multiple copies of the rRNA components are found on chromosomes #13, #14, #15, #21, and #22.

Answer: True

47. LINES are often referred to as retrotransposons because the mechanism of transposition resembles that used by retroviruses.

Answer: True

Chapter 13

Multiple Choice Format

1. When considering the initiation of transcription, one often finds consensus sequences located in the region of the DNA where RNA polymerase(s) bind. Which are common consensus sequences?

    A.   CAAT, TATA
    B.   GGTTC, TTAT
    C.   TTTTAAAA, GGGGCCCC
    D.   any trinucleotide repeat
    E.   satellite DNAs

Answer: A

2. What is the name given to the three bases in a messenger RNA that bind to the anticodon of tRNA to specify an amino acid placement in a protein?

    A.   protein
    B.   anti-anticodon
    C.   cistron
    D.   rho
    E.   codon

Answer: E

3. An intron is a section of

    A.   protein that is clipped out posttranslationally.
    B.   RNA that is removed during RNA processing.
    C.   DNA that is removed during DNA processing.
    D.   transfer RNA that binds to the anticodon.
    E.   carbohydrate that serves as a signal for RNA transport.

Answer: B

Sample Questions: Chapter 13 The Genetic Code and Transcription

4. The genetic code is fairly consistent among all organisms. The term often used to describe such consistency in the code is

    A.   universal.
    B.   exceptional.
    C.   trans-specific.
    D.   overlapping.
    E.   none of the above

Answer: A

5. Which of the following two terms relates most closely to split genes?

    A.   5'-cap, 3'-poly-A tail
    B.   introns, exons
    C.   elongation, termination
    D.   transcription, translation
    E.   heteroduplex, homoduplex

Answer: B

6. Significant in the deciphering of the genetic code was the discovery of the enzyme polynucleotide phosphorylase. What was this enzyme used for?

    A.   the manufacture of synthetic RNA for cell-free systems
    B.   ribosomal translocation
    C.   peptide bond formation
    D.   production of ribosomal proteins
    E.   degradation of RNA

Answer: A

7. In 1964, Nirenberg and Leder used the triplet binding assay to determine specific codon assignments. A complex of which of the following components was trapped in the nitrocellulose filter?

    A.   ribosomes and DNA
    B.   free tRNAs
    C.   charged tRNA, RNA triplet, and ribosome
    D.   uncharged tRNAs and ribosomes
    E.   sense and antisense strands of DNA

Answer: C

Sample Questions: Chapter 13 The Genetic Code and Transcription

8. What is the initiator triplet in both prokaryotes and eukaryotes? What amino acid is called in by this triplet?

      A.   UAA, no amino acid called in
      B.   UAA or UGA, arginine
      C.   AUG, arginine
      D.   AUG, methionine
      E.   UAA, methionine

Answer: D

9. Select three posttranscriptional modifications often seen in the maturation of mRNA in eukaryotes.

      A.   5'-capping, 3'-poly(A) tail addition, splicing
      B.   3'-capping, 5'-poly(A) tail addition, splicing
      C.   removal of exons, insertion of introns, capping
      D.   5-poly(A) tail addition, insertion of introns, capping
      E.   heteroduplex formation, base modification, capping

Answer: A

Short Answer Format

10. Describe the direction of information flow in living systems. Use appropriate, scientific terms in your description.

Answer: DNA is replicated and passed to offspring through a variety of reproductive processes. Information contained in the base sequences of DNA is transcribed into a variety of RNAs. Certain RNAs (tRNA) carry amino acids to the site of translation where proteins are assembled.

11. Describe the function of N-formylmethionine.

Answer: N-formylmethionine is a modified amino acid that serves as the starting amino acid in protein synthesis.

Sample Questions: Chapter 13 The Genetic Code and Transcription

12. What is polycistronic mRNA?

Answer: Polycistronic mRNA is seen primarily among prokaryotes, where one mRNA carries coding information and internal punctuation for the translation of more than one protein.

13. What is meant by punctuation in terms of the genetic code?

Answer: Certain triplets (AUG) commonly signal the start point for protein synthesis, while other triplets typically signal stop (UAA, UGA, UAG).

14. In the period from the late 1950s to the mid-1960s, numerous experiments using *in vitro* cell-free systems provided information on the nature of the genetic code.   Briefly outline significant experiments in the determination of the genetic code.

Answer: Use of polynucleotide phosphorylase for the random assembly of nucleotides provided for the assembly of RNA homo- and random heteropolymers, which when placed in the cell-free protein-synthesizing system, provided products (polypeptide chains) for analysis. The triplet binding assay and repeating copolymers were used to verify information provided earlier and to establish the ordered codon assignments.

15.   What is meant by the term *heterogeneous nuclear RNA (hnRNA)?*

Answer: pre-mRNA, primary transcripts before processing in eukaryotes

16.   "Cracking the Genetic Code" has been referred to as one of the most significant scientific achievements in modern times. Describe (in outline or brief statement form) the procedures used to "crack the code."

Answer:
- use of polynucleotide phosphorylase for the production of synthetic "mRNAs"
- introduction of synthetic mRNAs into the cell-free protein-synthesizing system
- frameshift mutations in the rII region of T4 phage to show code is triplet and
      degenerate
- triplet binding assay to produce mRNA-tRNA-ribosome complex
- development of regular copolymers for use in the cell-free protein-synthesizing
      system

Sample Questions: Chapter 13 The Genetic Code and Transcription

17. Describe how the sigma subunit of *E. coli* RNA polymerase participates in transcription.

Answer: The sigma subunit may give specificity to the RNA polymerase and play a regulatory role. It may be involved in the recognition of initiation sites or promoters.

18. The finding that virtually all organisms use the same genetic code provides the basis for declaring that the code is universal. Name two exceptions to such universality.

Answer: mitochondrial DNA, *Mycoplasma capricolum*, some protozoans

19. Suppose that in the use of polynucleotide phosphorylase, A and C are added in a ratio of 1A:5C. What is the probability for an AAA sequence occurring?

Answer: 1/6 X 1/6 X 1/6

20. Describe a difference between the RNA polymerases in eukaryotes and prokaryotes.

Answer: In eukaryotes, three polymerases (I, II, III) have been identified, while only one has been described in prokaryotes.

21. What two experimental procedures allowed deciphering of the ordered triplet assignments of the genetic code?

Answer: the triplet binding assay and the use of repeating RNA polymers with known sequence

22. Referring to the genetic code, what is meant by "wobble"?

Answer: relaxed pairing specificities in the third-base position

23. There is some indication that the code is in some way ordered; a certain pattern exists. What observations support this view?

Answer: Certain amino acids may be grouped according to the middle base -- for example, U or C in the second position often specifies hydrophobic amino acids.

Sample Questions: Chapter 13 The Genetic Code and Transcription

24. Describe four base triplets that are clearly responsible for punctuation (initiation, termination).

Answer: AUG (rarely GUG) for initiation; UAA, UGA, UAG for termination

25. What is the cause of a nonsense mutation?

Answer: when a termination triplet occurs in the coding region of a gene

26. In eukaryotes, what factors appear to encourage the specific association of RNA polymerase(s) to a specific region of DNA?

Answer: promoters, enhancers, and transcription factors

27. Regarding the efficient initiation of transcription by RNA polymerase II, what specific "upstream" signals appear to be involved?

Answer: TATA and CAAT base sequences, and enhancers

28. Sidney Brenner argued that the genetic code was nonoverlapping because he considered that coding restrictions would occur if it were overlapping. A second major argument against an overlapping code involved the effect of a single nucleotide change. In an overlapping code _____ adjacent amino acids would be affected by a point mutation, while in a nonoverlapping code _____ amino acid(s) would be affected.

Answer: two, one

29. A base at the first position of an anticodon on the tRNA would base pair with a base at the _____ position of the mRNA.

Answer: third

30. The relationship between codon and anticodon can be characterized as involving_____.

Answer: hydrogen bonds between complementary bases (usually) in typical antiparallel fashion

Sample Questions: Chapter 13 The Genetic Code and Transcription

31. If the three types of nucleic acids -- DNA, mRNA, tRNA -- which is most likely to contain modified bases?

Answer: tRNA

32. In the context of molecular genetics, how does one reconcile, the terms *overlapping genes* and *nonoverlapping code*?

Answer: The genetic code contains codons that are nonoverlapping; however, overlapping genes are observed in some viruses where, due to differential use of AUG to initiate translation, the same mRNA can yield different protein products.

True/False Format

33. An intron is a section of an RNA which gets spliced out.

Answer: True

34. Messenger RNA is usually polycistronic in eukaryotes.

Answer: False

35. Heterogeneous nuclear RNA is a primary transcript in eukaryotes that is processed prior to involvement in translation.

Answer: True

36. The enzyme polynucleotide phosphorylase is capable of generating a random assembly of ribonucleotides.

Answer: True

37. The genetic code is nonoverlapping, meaning that, assuming "standard translation," a given base participates in the specification of one and only one amino acid.

Answer: True

Sample Questions: Chapter 13 The Genetic Code and Transcription

38. Transcription factors function to help move ribosomes along the mRNA.

Answer: False

39. RNA processing occurs when amino acids are removed from nascent proteins.

Answer: False

40. A 3' poly-A tail and 5'cap are common components of prokaryotic RNAs.

Answer: False

41. When one speaks of a 5' cap, one is describing the addition of a base, usually thymine, to the 5' end of a completed peptide.

Answer: False

42. The triplet AUG is commonly used as a start codon during translation.

Answer: True

43. When considering genetic regulatory elements, *cis*-acting elements would be located on adjacent parts of the same DNA molecule.

Answer: True

44. Alternative splicing yields a group of mRNAs that, upon translation, result in a series of proteins called isoforms.

Answer: True

Chapter 14

Multiple Choice Format

1. Which of the following are among the major components of prokaryotic ribosomes?

     A.   12S rRNA, 5.8S rRNA, and proteins
     B.   16S rRNA, 5.8S rRNA, and 28S rRNA
     C.   16S rRNA, 5S rRNA, and 23S rRNA
     D.   lipids and carbohydrates
     E.   18S rRNA, 5.8S rRNA, and proteins

Answer: C

2. The term *peptidyltransferase* relates to

     A.   base additions during mRNA synthesis.
     B.   peptide bond formation during protein synthesis.
     C.   elongation factors binding to the large ribosomal subunit.
     D.   discontinuous strand replication.
     E.   5' capping of mRNA.

Answer: B

3. The one gene, one enzyme hypothesis emerged from work on which two organisms?

     A.   *E. coli* and yeast
     B.   *Drosophila* and humans
     C.   *Neurospora* and *Drosophila*
     D.   *E. coli* and humans
     E.   all of the above

Answer: C

Sample Questions: Chapter 14 Translation and Proteins

4. The β chain of adult hemoglobin is composed of 146 amino acids of a known sequence. In comparing the normal β chain with the β chain in sickle-cell hemoglobin, what alteration is one likely to find?

    A.   valine instead of glutamic acid in the sixth position
    B.   glutamic acid replacing valine in the first position
    C.   extensive amino acid substitutions
    D.   trinucleotide repeats
    E.   frameshift substitutions

Answer: A

5. The primary structure of a protein is determined by

    A.   the sequence of amino acids.
    B.   hydrogen bonds formed between the components of the peptide linkage.
    C.   a series of helical domains.
    D.   pleated sheets.
    E.   covalent bonds formed between fibroin residues.

Answer: A

6. One form of posttranslational modification of a protein includes

    A.   removal of introns.
    B.   shuffling of exons.
    C.   removal or modification of terminal amino acids.
    D.   removal of exons.
    E.   self-splicing.

Answer: C

7. Which protein class directly controls many of the metabolic reactions within a cell?

    A.   structural proteins
    B.   repressor proteins
    C.   operator proteins
    D.   enzymes
    E.   hydrophilic proteins

Answer: D

Sample Questions: Chapter 14 Translation and Proteins

8. The secondary structure of a protein includes the following elements:

    A.   gamma and delta
    B.   alpha and gamma
    C.   α-helix and β-pleated sheet
    D.   hydrophobic clusters
    E.   disulfide bridges

Answer: C

9. Side groups of amino acids are typically grouped under which of the following?

    A.   polar, nonpolar
    B.   linear, circular
    C.   alpha, omega
    D.   long, short
    E.   primary, secondary

Answer: A

Short Answer Format

10. During translation, chain termination is signaled by which triplets?

Answer: UAA, UGA, UAG

11. Below are listed several parameters relating to the structure and function of tRNA. Describe each.

    Four functional domains   Wobble hypothesis   Nonsense suppression

Answer:

    Four functional domains: amino acid attachment site, ribosome binding site, anticodon, aminoacyl synthetase binding site.

    Wobble hypothesis: The first two positions of the codon are precise in their complementary relationships. However, the third position is less specific.

    Nonsense suppression: often seen as a change in the anticodon of a tRNA so that a nonsense triplet now interacts with the mutant tRNA

Sample Questions: Chapter 14 Translation and Proteins

12. Provide a diagram of the process of translation involving two ribosomes, one mRNA, and at least four tRNA molecules. Include the following aspects in your presentation: 5' to 3' polarity restrictions for mRNA and tRNA, attachment site for the amino acids on the tRNA, and relative positions of ribosomal subunits.

Answer: Refer to the Klug and Cummings text and extend the mRNA to include another ribosome with its bound tRNAs. Notice that the amino acid is attached to the 3' end of the tRNA.

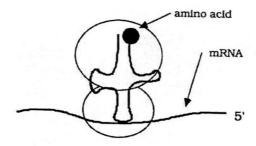

13. Draw and label the spatial and polarity relationships among the following translational components: ribosome (small and large subunits), growing polypeptide chains, amino acid attachment to tRNA, tRNA, mRNA, codon, anticodon.

Answer:

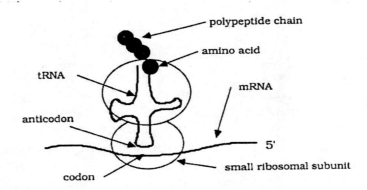

Sample Questions: Chapter 14 Translation and Proteins

14. Below is a drawing representing simultaneous transcription and translation in *E. coli*. Supply the correct response for the questions that follow. The direction of the RNA polymerase is shown by the arrow.

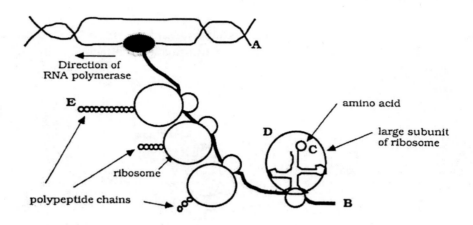

The letter A is nearest the 5' or 3' end of the molecule?

The letter B is nearest the 5' or 3' end of the molecule?

The letter C is nearest the 5' or 3' end of the tRNA molecule?

What is the "S" value for the large rRNA which is closest to the letter D?

The letter E is nearest the 5' or 3' end of the molecule?

Which terminus (N or C) of the growing polypeptide chain is nearest the letter E?

Answer: 3', 5', 3', 23S, N

15. Knowing that the base sequence of any given messenger RNA is responsible for precisely ordering the amino acids in a respective protein, present two mechanisms by which intrinsic properties of mRNA may regulate the "net output" of a given gene.

Answer: (1) "Net output" of a given gene may be influenced by the stability of a mRNA, and stability of a mRNA is determined in part by its base content and sequence. (2) Differential splicing of mRNA (actually mRNA precursors) can influence how much of a given product will be made from a gene.

Sample Questions: Chapter 14 Translation and Proteins

16. Name five potential forms of postranslational modification of proteins.

Answer:
1. removal or modification of terminal amino acids
2. modification of individual amino acids
3. attachment of carbohydrate side chains
4. removal of signal sequences
5. complex formation with metals

17. What are polyribosomes?

Answer: clusters of ribosomes held together by a mRNA

18. Below is a list of several phenomena relating to protein structure. Clearly describe each phenomenon, the conditions under which each occurs, and the probable influence each has on protein structure.

- Hydrophobic interactions
- Hydrogen bonds
- Disulfide bridges

Answer:

Hydrophobic interactions: Nonpolar side chains of amino acids tend to associate to form hydrophobic clusters usually away from the protein surface.

Hydrogen bonds: Such bonds may occur between the components of the peptide bond, the side chains, or a combination of the two. They are responsible for helical and pleated sheet structures of proteins.

Disulfide bridges: Such bonds are formed between two cysteine side chains and, because of their covalent nature, represent relatively strong attractive forces between different regions (sometimes distant) of proteins.

19. Early in the 1900s, Sir Archibald Garrod studied a number of metabolic defects in humans. One particular disorder involved the inability to metabolize homogentisic acid. What is the name of this disorder?

Answer: alkaptonuria

Sample Questions: Chapter 14 Translation and Proteins

20. Given the following table:

	Supplement 1	2	3	4
Strain A	+	-	+	-
Strain B	+	+	+	-
Strain C	+	+	+	+
Strain D	-	-	+	-

where numbers 1 through 4 indicate four supplements that must be added to sustain growth of the organism, determine a possible metabolic pathway that would give the results seen for the four mutant strains A through D.

Answer:

$$X \rightarrow + \rightarrow 4 \rightarrow + \rightarrow 2 \rightarrow + \rightarrow 1 \rightarrow + \rightarrow 3$$

C   B   A   D

21. Below is a table that presents the effect of different media on the growth response of tryptophan mutations in *Salmonella typhimurium* (+ = growth, - = no growth):

Strain	No Supplement	Medium Supplemented with			
		IGP	AA	IN	TRY
trp-8	-	+	+	+	+
trp-2	-	+	-	+	+
trp-3	-	-	-	+	+
trp-1	-	-	-	-	+

(a) Construct the biochemical pathway for the compounds IGP, AA, IN, and TRY based on these data.

(b) Place strains of bacteria (mutations) in the appropriate steps in the above pathway.

(c) In bacteria it is often possible to make partial diploid strains. Assume that a diploid strain was made containing the complete genomes of the *trp-2* and *trp-1* strains. Would this diploid strain be able to grow on the unsupplemented medium? Yes or no? Explain your answer.

Sample Questions: Chapter 14 Translation and Proteins

Answer:

(a)   →+→>AA→+→>IGP→+→>IN→+→Try

(b)   →+→>AA→+→>IGP→+→IN→+→Try

        ↑   ↑   ↑   ↑

        8   2   3   1

(c) Yes. Complementation will occur because the *trp-2* strain is also *trp-1*[+] and the *trp-1* strain is also *trp-2*[+].

22. The histidine locus is complex in *Neurospora crassa*. Many multiple alleles are known, such as *245*, *CD-16*, *430*, and *261*, which lack the ability to synthesize the amino acid histidine. Such strains will consequently be unable to grow on minimal medium. Provide an interpretation for the following observations involving these histidine strains of *Neurospora*.

(a) When heterokaryons are produced (single "cells" containing nuclei from two different strains), the combination of strains *245* and *261* always produces growth on minimal medium, whereas the combination of strains *CD*-16 and *245* never produces growth on minimal medium.

(b) When strain *430* is crossed with strain *261*, rare ascospores are produced that can grow on minimal medium.

Answer:

(a) There are at least two different functional domains (complementation groups) in the histidine locus; *CD*-16 and *245* are in the same domain, while *261* is in the other domain.

(b) Rare crossing over between mutation sites in strain *430* and strain *261* produces the wildtype gene.

23. Describe the conceptual basis for constructing biochemical pathways using nutrient supplement experiments with *Neurospora*.

Answer: The substance, which when added to minimal medium "cures" the largest number of strains, must be toward the end of the pathway. A supplement that fails to "cure" many strains must be early in the pathway.

Sample Questions: Chapter 14 Translation and Proteins

24. Below is a set of experimental results relating the growth (+) of *Neurospora* on several media (MM = minimal medium). Based on the information provided, present the biochemical pathway and the locations of the metabolic blocks.

| | | Medium | |
| | MM | MM+A | MM+B |
Strain			
*t*409	-	+	+
*t*410	+	+	+
*r*3	-	-	+

Answer:

$$→+→A →+→ B$$
$$\uparrow \qquad \uparrow$$
$$t409 \qquad r3$$

25. The problem below relates to the synthesis of several intermediates in the citric acid cycle, which is essential in the production of ATP through aerobic respiration. A set of experimental results relating the growth (+) of *Neurospora* on several media is given in the table. Based on the information provided, present the biochemical pathway for the substances oxaloacetate, fumarate, malate, and succinate, and the locations of the metabolic blocks produced by the various strains.

Strain	MM	MM + oxaloacetate	MM + fumarate	MM + malate	MM + succinate
162	-	+	-	+	-
136	-	+	-	-	-
141	-	+	+	+	-

MM = minimal medium

Answer:

$$\text{succinate} →+→ \text{fumarate}→+→ \text{malate} →+→\text{oxaloacetate}$$
$$\uparrow \qquad\qquad \uparrow \qquad\qquad \uparrow$$
$$141 \qquad\qquad 162 \qquad\qquad 136$$

Sample Questions: Chapter 14 Translation and Proteins

26. Three major types of RNAs were discussed in some detail; mRNA, rRNA, and tRNA. For each of the conditions below, predict the consequences in terms of the population of proteins being synthesized in a particular cell. What type of change, if any, is expected in the individual protein involved (if one is involved)?

(a) An acridine dye-induced mutation (adds or deletes single bases in DNA) leads to a mRNA for one protein-producing gene. The condition is heterozygous in the involved cell.

population of proteins:
individual protein:

(b) A deletion (homozygous) that removes approximately half of the rRNA genes.

population of proteins:
individual protein:

Answer:

(a) Population of proteins: Half of the protein products of that gene will be defective, the other half will be normal. Individual protein: The protein should show multiple amino acid substitutions "downstream" from the point of the mutation. If a nonsense triplet is introduced, the protein would be shortened in the substituted region.

(b) Population of proteins: There would be an overall reduction in protein synthesis. Individual proteins: All of the proteins would be made in their normal form, but at reduced levels.

27. Given below is a hypothetical "wild type" polypeptide containing twelve amino acids (each letter represents one amino acid). Assume that gene X is responsible for its synthesis.

A-B-C-D-E-F-G-H-I-J-K-L

The amino acid "A" is at the C terminus and amino acid "L" is at the N terminus. Present sequences of amino acids from gene X under the following circumstances. In other words, modify the sequence (if appropriate) and write it down under each of the statements below:

(a) A substitution of adenine for cytosine in the 7th base in the coding region of the mRNA (counting from the 5' end of the coding region of the mRNA).

(b) A frameshift mutation (adds or deletes single bases in DNA) resulting in an insertion of a base between the 9th and 10th positions of the coding region of the mRNA (counting from the 5' end of the coding region of the mRNA).

(c) A nonsense mutation (fails to code for an amino acid) involving bases 4, 5, and 6 in the coding region of the mRNA (counting from the 5' end of the coding region of the mRNA).

Sample Questions: Chapter 14 Translation and Proteins

Answer:

(a)   A-B-C-D-E-F-G-H-I-**Q**-K-L
(b)   **O-S-E-Y-I-U-T-S-R**-J-K-L
(c)   -L

28. A series of mutations in the bacterium *Salmonella typhimurium* results in the requirement of either tryptophan or some related molecule in order for growth to occur.

Strain	Medium				
	MM	MM + AA	MM + IGP	MM + Indole	MM + tryptophan
trp-8	-	+	+	+	+
trp-2	-	-	+	+	+
trp-3	-	-	-	+	+
trp-1	-	-	-	-	+

MM = minimal medium   AA = anthranilic acid   IGP = indole glycerol phosphate

(a) From the data above, provide a biosynthetic pathway for tryptophan.
(b) Place mutations in the appropriate places in the above pathway.
(c) Assuming that a diploid organism could be made by combining the genomes of the *trp*-8 and *trp*-1 strains, would growth occur on the MM medium? (yes or no?)
(d)   In this diploid would you say that complementation occurred? (yes or no?)

Answer:

(a)   AA → IGP →Indole → Tryptophan

(b)   →+→AA →+→IGP →+→ Indole →+→Tryptophan
        ↑   ↑   ↑   ↑
      trp-8   *trp*-2   *trp*-3   *trp*-1

(c)   yes

(d)   yes

Sample Questions: Chapter 14 Translation and Proteins

29. Phenylketonuria is a recessive metabolic disease caused by the absence of the enzyme phenylalanine hydroxylase. What is the phenotype of the disease, and what causes the phenotype to develop?

Answer: Mental retardation is thought to be caused by the buildup of phenylalanine and its derivatives.

30. Much has been learned about the relationship between genes and gene products through the use of the mold *Neurospora*. What specific attributes make *Neurospora* a good organism for such studies?

Answer: knowledge of its biochemistry, it has haploid ascospores, nutritional mutations can be isolated with relative ease

31. Describe the basic structure of normal adult hemoglobin and the abnormality observed in sickle-cell hemoglobin.

Answer: The predominant form of adult hemoglobin is composed of two α and two β chains. In sickle-cell hemoglobin, the sixth amino acid in the β chain is valine instead of glutamic acid.

32. What is the general populational distribution of the sickle-cell gene in the United States??

Answer: The gene is most common among African-Americans.

33. What are *chaperones*?

Answer: Chaperones function to facilitate the folding of other proteins.

34. In what ways do the amino acid side chains interact to influence protein function?

Answer: Higher level folding of proteins is dependent on a variety of interactions (ionic, covalent, hydrogen, hydrophobic, hydrophilic, etc.) *which* determine the functional three dimensional structure of proteins.

Sample Questions: Chapter 14 Translation and Proteins

35. Assuming that a protein is 250 amino acids long, how many different molecules, each with a unique sequence, could be formed?

Answer: 20^{250}

36. Regarding the protein structure, how are β-pleated sheets formed?

Answer: Several chains run in parallel or antiparallel fashion, stabilized by hydrogen bonds formed between components of the peptide linkage.

37. Considering the types of side chains on amino acids and their relationship to protein structure, where are the amino acids with hydrophobic side chains most likely to be located?

Answer: away from the water environment and in the interior portion of the molecule

38. Present two forms of posttranslational modification of proteins.

Answer: removal of terminal amino acids, modification (phosphorylation, glycosylation) of side chains

39. Regarding phenylketonuria (PKU), what therapeutic procedures are applied?

Answer: screening of newborns and a low phenylalanine diet

40. Nutritional mutants in *Neurospora* can be "cured" by treating the medium with substances in the defective metabolic pathway. Under what condition is the mutant strain (auxotroph) "cured"?

Answer: if the substance added occurs after the metabolic block

41. Studies of *Neurospora* led to the _____ statement, whereas studies of human hemoglobin led to the _____ statement .

Answer: one-gene:one-enzyme, one-gene:one-polypeptide

Sample Questions: Chapter 14 Translation and Proteins

42. A procedure that often used to separate molecules by using their molecular charges is called_____.

Answer: electrophoresis

43. Electrophoretic separation of HbA from HbS is based on a difference in their_____.

Answer: charge

44. Briefly describe what is meant by the term *exon shuffling*.

Answer: In the 1970s, Walter Gilbert suggested that the functional regions of genes in eukaryotes consist of collections of exons originally present in ancestral genes that are brought together through various recombinational events over time.

45. Assume that a base addition occurs early in the coding region of a gene. Is the protein product of this gene expected to have *more* or *fewer* altered amino acids compared to the original gene with a base deletion late in the coding region?

Answer: more

True/False Format

46. Proteins are composed of strings of nucleotides connected together by 5'-3' phosphodiester bonds.

Answer: False

47. The ribonucleic acid components known to exist in eukaryotic ribosomes are the following: 5.8S, 18S, 28S, 5S.

Answer: True

48. Prokaryotic and eukaryotic ribosomes are structurally and chemically identical.

Answer: False

Sample Questions: Chapter 14 Translation and Proteins

49. rDNA is the portion of a genome involved in the production of ribosomal RNA.

Answer: True

50. The secondary structure of a protein is dependent on polar interactions among the side chains of the amino acids.

Answer: False

51. The primary structure of a protein is composed of the sequence of amino acids in that protein.

Answer: True

52. Sickle-cell anemia is caused by the absence of the alpha chain of hemoglobin.

Answer: False

53. When a metabolic block occurs in a biochemical pathway, it is common for the substance immediately prior to that block to accumulate in amount.

Answer: True

Sample Questions: Chapter 15 Gene Mutation, DNA Repair, and
Transposable Elements

Chapter 15

Multiple Choice Format

1. Mutations that arise in nature, from no particular artificial agent, are called

    A.   natural mutations.
    B.   induced mutations.
    C.   spontaneous mutations.
    D.   chromosomal aberrations.
    E.   cosmic mutations.

Answer: C

2. Nutritional mutations can be defined as

    A.   mutations that do not allow an organism to grow on minimal medium.
         but do allow the organism to grow on complete medium.
    B.   mutations that change the composition of the medium.
    C.   belonging to the group called prototrophs.
    D.   mutations caused by site-specific mutagenesis.
    E.   all strains that are not auxotrophic.

Answer: A

3. Assume that you are examining a series of human pedigrees and observe the following: more males abnormal than females; approximately half the grandsons of abnormal males, abnormal; some females abnormal but usually only if their maternal grandfather was abnormal and their mother married an abnormal male. What type of inheritance might be occurring?

    A.   sex-linked recessive
    B.   autosomal dominant, sex-limited
    C.   sex-linked dominant
    D.   Y-linked dominant
    E.   multiple factor

Answer: A

Sample Questions: Chapter 15 Gene Mutation, DNA Repair, and Transposable Elements

4. Two formal terms used to describe categories of mutational nucleotide substitutions in DNA are

 A. base analogues and frameshift.
 B. error prone and spontaneous.
 C. transversions and transitions.
 D. euchromatic and heterochromatic.
 E. sense and antisense.

Answer: C

5. Name two mutagens would be classified as base analogues.

 A. acridine orange and proflavin
 B. ethylmethane sulfonate and ethylmethylketone peroxide
 C. ultraviolet light and cosmic radiation
 D. 5-bromouracil and 2-aminopurine
 E. hydroxyurea and peroxidase

Answer: D

6. A class of mutations that results in multiple contiguous amino acid changes in proteins is likely to be which of the following?

 A. base analogue
 B. transversion
 C. transition
 D. frameshift
 E. recombinant

Answer: D

Sample Questions: Chapter 15 Gene Mutation, DNA Repair, and Transposable Elements

7. Ultraviolet light causes pyrimidine dimers to form in DNA. Some individuals are genetically incapable of repairing some dimers at "normal" rates. Such individuals are likely to suffer from

     A.   xeroderma pigmentosum.
     B.   SCID.
     C.   phenylketonuria.
     D.   muscular dystrophy.
     E.   Huntington disease.

Answer: A

Short Answer Format

8. Assume that you are working with a mutant, nutritionally deficient strain of *Escherichia coli* and isolate "revertants," which are nutritional-normal. Describe, at the molecular level, possible causes for the "reversion to wild type."

Answer: Two general classes of events could be involved: true reversion or suppression. True reversion would involve a precise correction of the original mutation. Suppression could be intragenic or intergenic. In intragenic suppression, a change in some other part of the mutant gene product serves to "compensate" for the original mutation. In intergenic suppression, a mutation in some other gene, such as a transfer RNA, serves to "compensate" for the original mutation.

9. Present a general description (diagram) of a typical transposable element, and give an example of transposable elements, one each, in corn and *Drosophila*.

Answer: For diagrams, see the appropriate figures in the Klug and Cummings text. Corn = *Ac*, *Drosophila* = *copia*

10. Present a description of the mutagenic action of any two of the following mutagens: 5-bromouracil, proflavin, ultraviolet light.

Answer: 5-bromouracil is an analogue of thymine, which anomalously pairs with guanine. Proflavin adds or removes single bases from DNA, thus causing frameshift mutations. Ultraviolet light causes thymine dimers.

11. Some mutagens cause genetic changes that can be "corrected" by re-exposing cells to the same mutagen. Other mutagens do not behave in this way. Provide one example of each of these two types of agents, and describe the mutational changes caused in DNA. Explain why some mutagens behave in one way while others do not.

Answer: Mutagens that cause base substitutions are "corrected" by mutagens of the same class (nitrous acid, 2-aminopurine, and 5-bromouracil). Frameshift mutations, caused by proflavin or acridine orange, are "corrected" by the same class of frameshift mutagens, but not by mutagens that cause base substitutions. X rays cause major structural changes in chromosomes (deletions, translocations, etc.) and are not "corrected" by any mutagen, including X-rays.

12. Explain why a "+ -" combination of frameshift mutations may give a wildtype phenotype whereas a "- +" combination may give a mutant phenotype even though the sites of insertion/deletion are the same.

Answer: A frameshift in the "- +"direction may have introduced a nonsense triplet which was not introduced, by chance, by the "+-" combination.

13. Mutations may exert a variety of effects on living systems. List at least three categories of mutations.

Answer: morphological mutations, nutritional or biochemical mutations, behavioral mutations, regulatory mutations, lethal mutations, conditional mutations

14. Under certain conditions, the rate of mutation of a particular gene may be determined in humans. What conditions would favor the most direct determination of mutation rate in humans?

Answer: dominant, fully expressed, 100% penetrant, single locus

15. In a survey of 240,000 human births, six achondroplastic births were recorded to parents who were unaffected. Given that this form of dwarfism is caused by a fully penetrant, dominant, autosomal gene, what is the mutation rate?

Answer: $6/(4.8 \times 10^5)$

Sample Questions: Chapter 15 Gene Mutation, DNA Repair, and Transposable Elements

16. Three human disorders -- fragile-X syndrome, myotonic dystrophy, and Huntington disease-- are conceptually linked by a common mode of molecular upset. Describe the phenomena that link these disorders.

Answer: All three are caused by disparate genes, but each gene was found to contain repeats of a unique trinucleotide sequence. In addition, the number of repeats may increase in each subsequent generation (genetic anticipation).

17. What is meant by the term *photoreactivation repair*?

Answer: Photoreactivation repair, discovered in 1949, is a process described in *E. coli* in which UV-induced DNA damage can be partially reversed if cells are briefly exposed to light in the blue range of the visible spectrum.

18. List five general categories of mutation.

Answer: induced, spontaneous, morphological, nutritional/biochemical, behavioral, regulatory, lethal, conditional

19. What chromosomal complements are present in progeny of crosses between attached-X females and normal males?

Answer: triplo-X females that die; viable attached-X females (XXY); viable XY males, YY zygotes that die

20. Describe how acridine dyes cause frameshift mutations.

Answer: intercalation between bases of intact DNA

21. Regarding the nature of the ABO blood groups, what condition leads to the O blood type?

Answer: failure to modify the H substance due to lack of glycosyltransferase activity

Sample Questions: Chapter 15 Gene Mutation, DNA Repair, and Transposable Elements

22. Under what condition(s) might one have an amino acid substitution in a protein that does not result in an altered phenotype?

Answer: The possibility of a change in protein function, therefore phenotype, depends on the location and chemical properties of the involved amino acid(s).

23. Recent discoveries on causes of fragile-X syndrome, myotonic dystrophy, and Huntington disease indicate what type of genetic alteration?

Answer: changes in trinucleotide repeats

24. What is the Ames test, and how does it work?

Answer: Four tester strains of *Salmonella typhimurium* are used to test for sensitivity and specificity of mutagenesis.

25. What is the common influence of ultraviolet light on DNA?

Answer: generation of pyrimidine dimers

26. Describe the phenomenon of photoreactivation repair.

Answer: Described by A. Kelner in 1949, photoreactivation repair is mediated by the photoreactivation enzyme (PRE), which cleaves covalent bonds between the dimers.

27. The process of error correction of mismatched bases carried out by DNA polymerases is called

Answer: proofreading.

28. Recombinational repair is activated when damaged DNA has escaped repair and the distortion disrupts the process of replication that depends on the product of which gene?

Answer: *rec*A

Sample Questions: Chapter 15 Gene Mutation, DNA Repair, and Transposable Elements

29. What human condition is caused by unrepaired UV-induced lesions?

Answer: xeroderma pigmentosum

30. When X rays penetrate cells, electrons are ejected from atoms of molecules. Stable molecules can be transformed into what types of hazardous materials?

Answer: free radicals and reactive ions

31. Site-directed mutagenesis is a technique used to study specific aspects of mutant genes. What is the specific technical goal of site-specific mutagenesis?

Answer: to alter one or more specific nucleotides with a gene in order to change a specific codon

32. Describe the *Alu* family of mobile elements in humans.

Answer: The *Alu* family consists of about 300,000 copies of 200 - 300 base pair sequence interspersed throughout the genome.

33. Three major types of RNAs were discussed in some detail; mRNA, rRNA, and tRNA. For each of the conditions below predict the consequences in terms of the population of proteins being synthesized in a particular cell. What type of change, if any, is expected in the individual protein involved (if one is involved)?

(a) An acridine dye-induced mutation in mRNA . The condition is heterozygous in the involved cell.

population of proteins:

individual protein:

(b) A deletion (homozygous) which removes approximately half of the rRNA genes.

population of proteins:

individual protein:

Sample Questions: Chapter 15 Gene Mutation, DNA Repair, and Transposable Elements

Answer:

(a) Population of proteins: Half of the protein products of that gene will be defective, the other half will be normal. Individual protein: The protein should show multiple amino acid substitutions "downstream" from the point of the mutation. If a nonsense triplet is introduced, the protein would be shortened in the substituted region.

(b) Population of proteins: There would be an overall reduction in protein synthesis. Individual proteins: All of the proteins would be made in their normal form, but at reduced levels.

34. Given below is a hypothetical "wild type" polypeptide containing twelve amino acids (each letter arbitrarily represents one amino acid). Assume that gene X is responsible for its synthesis.

A-B-C-D-E-F-G-H-I-J-K-L

The amino acid "A" is at the C terminus and amino acid "L" is at the N terminus. Present sequences of amino acids from gene X under the following circumstances. In other words, modify the sequence (if appropriate) and write it down under each of the statements below:

(a) A substitution of adenine for cytosine in the 7th base in the coding region of the mRNA (counting from the 5' end of the coding region of the mRNA).

(b) A frameshift mutation resulting in an insertion of a base between the 9th and 10th positions of the coding region of the mRNA (counting from the 5' end of the coding region of the mRNA).

(c) A nonsense mutation involving bases 4, 5, and 6 in the coding region of the mRNA (counting from the 5' end of the coding region of the mRNA).

Answers:

(a)   A-B-C-D-E-F-G-H-I-**Q**-K-L

(b)   **O-S-E-Y-I-U-T-S-R**-J-K-L

(c)   -L

Sample Questions: Chapter 15 Gene Mutation, DNA Repair, and Transposable Elements

35. Name two chemical mutagens that are collectively called acridine dyes.

Answer: proflavin and acridine orange

36. One type of mutation involves the replacement of a purine with a purine, while another causes the replacement of a pyrimidine with a purine. What general terms are associated with these two mutational phenomena?

Answer: transition and transversion, respectively

37. In general, mutation rates in humans occur in the range of _____ per gamete per generation.

Answer: 10^{-5} to 10^{-6}

38. Assuming one mutational event in a gene, on average, which of the following mutagens would be expected to cause the most damage to a protein synthesized by such a mutagenized gene? 5-bromouracil, 2-amino purine, ethylmethane sulfonate, acridine orange

Answer: acridine orange

True/False Format

39. Of the two cell lines that can contain a mutation in an organism, somatic and germ line, the latter is most consequential to subsequent generations.

Answer: True

40. Certain base analogues, such as 5-bromouracil, cause mutations by chemically altering nitrogenous bases in nonreplicating DNA.

Answer: False

Sample Questions: Chapter 15 Gene Mutation, DNA Repair, and Transposable Elements

41. When treating an organism with a mutagen, while it is possible that homozygous mutations will occur, it is more likely that most new mutations will be heterozygous or hemizygous.

Answer: True

42. The shorter the wavelength of a radiation source, the greater its likelihood of causing damage.

Answer: True

43. Acridine orange is an alkylating agent.

Answer: False

44. While mutation is the original source of genetic variation, its influence on changing gene frequencies is relatively minor.

Answer: True

45. When using the attached-X method of mutation assessment in *Drosophila*, sons inherit their X chromosome from their mother and their Y chromosome from their father.

Answer: False

46. When using the attached-X method of mutation assessment in *Drosophila*, sons inherit their X chromosome from their father and their Y chromosome from their mother.

Answer: True

47. Pyrimidine dimers are typically caused by the mutagen 2-amino purine.

Answer: False

48. A missense mutation causes premature chain (protein) termination.

Answer: False

Chapter 16

Multiple Choice Format

1. What term refers to a contiguous genetic complex that is under coordinate control?

      A.   lysogen
      B.   prototroph
      C.   operon
      D.   allosteric
      E.   attenuation

Answer: C

2. Genetic regulation in eukaryotes can take place at a variety of levels from transcriptional to posttranslational. At what level is genetic regulation considered most likely in prokaryotes?

      A.   transcriptional
      B.   capping
      C.   polyadenylation of the 3' end of the mRNAs
      D.   intron processing
      E.   exon processing

Answer: A

3. What term would be applied to a regulatory condition that occurs when protein greatly reduces transcription when associated with a particular section of DNA?

      A.   negative control
      B.   positive control
      C.   inhibition
      D.   activation
      E.   stimulation

Answer: A

Sample Questions: Chapter 16   Regulation of Gene Expression

4. Which term most appropriately refers to a regulatory protein in prokaryotes?

    A.   translation
    B.   RNA processing
    C.   DNA binding protein
    D.   gyrase action
    E.   helicase activation

Answer: C

5. In the *lactose* operon, the product of structural gene *lacZ* is capable of

    A.   nonautonomous replication.
    B.   forming lactose from two glucose molecules.
    C.   replacing hexokinase in the early steps of glycolysis.
    D.   splitting the β-linkage of lactose.
    E.   forming ATP from pyruvate.

Answer: D

6. Which of the following terms best characterizes catabolite repression associated with the *lactose* operon in *E. coli*?

    A.   inducible system
    B.   repressible system
    C.   negative control
    D.   positive control
    E.   constitutive

Answer: D

7. When referring to attenuation in regulation of the *tryptophan* operon, it would be safe to say that when there are high levels of tryptophan available to the organism _____

    A.   the *tryptophan* operon is being transcribed at relatively high levels.
    B.   translational termination is likely.
    C.   transcriptional termination is likely.
    D.   tryptophan is inactivating the repressor protein.
    E.   ribosomes are stalling during translation of the attenuator region.

Answer: C

Sample Questions: Chapter 16 Regulation of Gene Expression

8. Which of the following clusters of terms applies when addressing *enhancers* as elements associated with eukaryotic genetic regulation?

    A.   *cis*-acting, variable orientation, variable position
    B.   *trans*-acting, fixed position, fixed orientation
    C.   *cis*-acting, fixed position, fixed orientation
    D.   *cis*-acting, variable position, fixed orientation
    E.   *trans*- and *cis*-acting, variable position

Answer: A

9. Two modular elements that appear as consensus sequences upstream from RNA polymerase II transcription start sites are

    A.   microsatellites and transposons.
    B.   rDNA and nucleolar organizers.
    C.   TATA and CAAT.
    D.   TTAA and CCTT.
    E.   enhancers and telomeres.

Answer: C

10. Regarding eukaryotic and prokaryotic genetic regulation, what process seems to be the most similar between the two?

    A.   transcriptional regulation
    B.   RNA splicing regulation
    C.   intron/exon shuffling
    D.   5'-capping regulation
    E.   poly-A tail addition

Answer: A

11. DNA methylation may be a significant mode of genetic regulation in eukaryotes. Methylation refers to

    A.   altering RNA polymerase activity by methylation.
    B.   changes in DNA-DNA hydrogen binding.
    C.   altering translational activity especially of highly methylated tRNAs.
    D.   alteration of DNA polymerase activity by addition of methyl groups to glycine residues.
    E.   addition of methyl groups to the cytosine of CG doublets.

Answer: E

Sample Questions: Chapter 16 Regulation of Gene Expression

Short Answer Format

12. Certain mutations in the regulator gene of the *lac* system in *E coli* result in maximal synthesis of the Lac proteins (β-galactosidase, etc.) even in the absence of the inducer (lactose). Provide an explanation for this observation.

Answer: There has been a mutation in the gene that produces the repressor, or the operator is mutated so that it will not interact with the repressor.

13. Present a detailed description of the actions of the regulatory proteins in inducible and repressible enzyme systems.

Answer: Inducible system: the repressor is normally active but the inducer inactivates the repressor. Repressible system: the repressor is inactive but is activated by the corepressor. Active repressors turn off transcription.

14. Compare and contrast positive and negative control of gene expression in bacteria.

Answer: Both forms of control result from an interaction of a molecule (usually considered to be a protein) with the genetic material (either RNA or DNA). Positive control results when the interaction stimulates transcription, whereas negative control occurs when the interaction inhibits transcription.

15. (a) Describe by labeled diagram the structural components of the *lactose* operon in *E coli*. (b) State the function of the *lac* regulator gene. (c) State the function of β-galactosidase in the *lac* system. (d) Show by diagram the manner in which lactose brings about transcription of the three structural genes of the *lac* operon. (e) Explain why certain mutations in the regulator gene (Γ) of the *lac* system result in maximal synthesis of β-galactosidase, permease, and transacetylase even in the absence of the inducer (lactose).

Answer:

(a)   See appropriate diagrams in the Klug and Cummings text.
(b)   The regulator gene produces a repressor protein that interacts with the operator to shut off transcription. In the presence of lactose, the repressor protein does not interact with the operator.
(c)   β-galactosidase cleaves the lactose sugar into its components glucose and galactose.
(d)   See appropriate diagrams in the Klug and Cummings text.
(e)   Such mutations provide modified proteins that are unable to associate with the operator to shut off transcription.

Sample Questions: Chapter 16   Regulation of Gene Expression

16. The table below lists several genotypes associated with the *lac* operon in *E. coli*. For each, indicate with a "+" or a "-" whether β-galactosidase would be expected to be produced at induced levels.

β-galactosidase production

Genotype — **No Lactose   On Lactose**

(a) $I^+ O^+ Z^+ / F' I^- O^+ Z^+$
(b) $I^- O^c Z^+ / F' I^- O^+ Z$
(c) $I^s O^c Z^+ / F' I^+ O^+ Z^+$
(d) $I^- O^+ Z^+ / F' I^- O^+ Z^+$

I^+ = wild type repressor
I^- = mutant repressor (unable to bind to the operator)
I^s = mutant repressor (insensitive to lactose)
O^+ = wild type operator
O^c = constitutive operator (insensitive to repressor)

Answer:

	No Lactose	On Lactose
(a)	-	+
(b)	+	+
(c)	+	+
(d)	+	+

17. The table below lists several genotypes associated with the *lac* operon in *E. coli*. For each, indicate with a "+" or a "-" whether β-galactosidase would be expected to be produced at induced levels.

β-galactosidase production

Genotype — **No Lactose   On Lactose**

(a) $I^+ O^+ Z^+ / F' I^+ O^+ Z^+$
(b) $I^- O^c Z / F' I^- O^c Z$
(c) $I^- O^c Z^+ / F' I^- O^+ Z^+$
(d) $I^s O^c Z / F' I^s O^+ Z^+$

I^+ = wild type repressor
I^- = mutant repressor (unable to bind to the operator)
I^s = mutant repressor (insensitive to lactose)
O^+ = wild type operator
O^c = constitutive operator (insensitive to repressor)

Sample Questions: Chapter 16 Regulation of Gene Expression

Answer:

(a)   -   +
(b)   -   -
(c)   +   +
(d)   -   -

18. State whether the following statement is true or false, then give your reasoning. The terminating "hairpin" loop occurs in the tryptophan operon when sufficient tryptophan is present.

Answer: True; the "hairpin" loops terminates transcription.

19. Describe what is meant by a *gratuitous inducer*. Give an example.

Answer: A gratuitous inducer is a chemical analogue of a natural inducer. It serves as an inducer but is not a substrate for the reactions related to the natural inducer. Isopropylthiogalactoside (IPTG) is a gratuitous inducer of the *lactose* operon.

20. Describe the positive control exerted by the catabolite activating protein (CAP). Include a description of catabolite repression.

Answer: Regarding regulation of the *lac* operon, in the absence of glucose, CAP (dependent on cAMP and adenyl cyclase) binds to the CAP site and facilitates transcription (positive control). Transcription of the operon is inhibited in the presence of glucose (catabolite repression).

21. Present an overview of prokaryotic regulation in terms of growth efficiency.

Answer: Genetic systems have evolved that allow for "inhouse" production of growth substances when not supplied in the environment or when in full supply. When needed substances are in full supply, certain such genetic systems are repressed.

22. Within the control region of the *tryptophan* operon is a section of DNA that is sensitive to levels of tryptophan in the system. What is the name of this region?

Answer: Leader or attenuator region

Sample Questions: Chapter 16 Regulation of Gene Expression

23. Given the diagram below, what type of control, positive or negative, is operating?

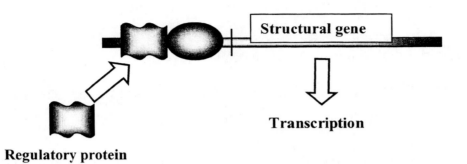

Answer: positive

24. Regrading regulation of the *tryptophan* operon, what might one appropriately call the amino acid tryptophan?

Answer: corepressor

25. Mutations in the *lacI* and *lacO* genes in the *lactose* system often lead to full production of the three structural genes related to the *lac* operon, even with no lactose available to the organism. Such mutations would be called_____.

Answer: constitutive

26. A constitutive mutation may be of several types in the *lac* operon. Name two types of constitutive mutation.

Answer: *lacI⁻* and *lacOᶜ*

27. What is the function of the *lac*Y gene in the *lactose* operon?

Answer: The *lac*Y gene codes for β-galactoside permease, a membrane-bound protein that transports lactose into the bacterial cell.

Sample Questions: Chapter 16 Regulation of Gene Expression

28. Explain why $lacO^c$ mutations are *cis*-acting while *lac*I mutations can be *trans*-acting.

Answer: The operator region does not produce a diffusible product, while the *lac*I gene does.

29. What experimental results would indicate that the mutation $lacI^s$ is dominant to $lacI^+$?

Answer: In $lacI^s$ / $lacI^+$ partial diploids, the *lac* operon is in a repressed state in the presence of lactose.

30. Monod discovered that if tryptophan is present in relatively high quantities in the growth medium, the enzymes necessary for its synthesis are repressed. How does this occur?

Answer: Tryptophan acts as a corepressor to activate the tryptophan repressor protein; it also is involved in an attenuation system, which causes termination of transcription.

31. When considering the binding of cAMP-CAP and RNA polymerase to the *lac* operon, both bind more efficiently than either does alone. What term is applied to this increased efficiency of binding?

Answer: cooperative binding

32. An allosteric molecule is one in which _____.

Answer: there is more than one binding site

33. What symbols are used to describe constitutive mutations in the *lac* system?

Answer: I^- and O^c

34. Regarding the *tryptophan* operon, $trpR^-$ maps a considerable distance from the structural genes. The mutation either inhibits the interaction with tryptophan or inhibits repressor formation entirely. In the presence of tryptophan in the medium, would you expect the *tryptophan* operon to be transcriptionally active? Explain.

Answer: With either of the two scenarios mentioned in the problem, the absence of repressor function in a repressible system means that there would be no repression of the operon. The operon would be transcriptionally active.

Sample Questions: Chapter 16   Regulation of Gene Expression

35. The catabolite repression system in *E. coli* essentially represses the *lac* operon when glucose is present. What evolutionary advantage would favor evolution of such a system?

Answer: Glucose can enter glycolysis "as is," while lactose must first be split into glucose and galactose. To do so, the energy-requiring synthesis of β-galactosidase is required. It is more energy-efficient to burn glucose than lactose.

36. Enhancers are said to be *cis*-acting. What is meant by *cis*-acting and what are enhancers?

Answer: *Cis*-acting means that the genes under control must be in the same chromosome as the *cis*-acting element. Enhancers are sections of DNA which regulate transcription of other sections of DNA.

37. Describe three characteristics of enhancers.

Answer: position need not be fixed, orientation may be inverted without significant effect; they are not gene-specific

38. What is the significance of the homeodomain?

Answer: The homeodomain is a highly conserved protein of 60 amino acids found in a variety of organisms, which, in conjunction with other factors (POU domains), are thought to play a role in DNA binding and transcriptional activation.

39. Transcription factors appear to be important molecules relating to the regulation of gene activity. Regarding eukaryotes, two general classes exist. Briefly describe each.

Answer: One class assembles at promoter regions adjacent to the site of transcription. The other class binds at more distant regions (enhancers).

40. What are zinc fingers, and why are they frequently encountered in descriptions of genetic regulation in eukaryotes?

Answer: Zinc fingers consist of amino acid sequences containing two cysteine and two histidine residues at repeating intervals. Interspersed cysteine and histidine residues covalently bind zinc atoms, folding the amino acids into loops (zinc fingers). They are one of the major groups of eukaryotic transcription factors. They were originally discovered in the *Xenopus,* and this structural motif has been identified in a variety of significant regulatory circumstances, including proto-oncogenes and developmental control genes in *Drosophila*.

Sample Questions: Chapter 16 Regulation of Gene Expression

41. Describe the function and general nature of promoters in eukaryotes.

Answer: Promoter regions are necessary for the initiation of transcription. Promoters that interact with RNA polymerase II are usually located within 100 bp upstream of a gene and usually contain a TATA box and a CAAT box.

42. What is meant by the term *helix-turn-helix* (HTH)?

Answer: HTH domains were the first DNA-binding motifs to be identified. They are found in the *cro*, *lac*, and *trp* repressors. A geometric conformation is formed by two adjacent α-helices separated by a "turn" of several amino acids. Such motifs bind to the major groves of DNA and interact with the DNA backbone. They are present in developmentally significant sections of DNA called homeoboxes.

43. What is a homeobox, and what is its significance?

Answer: A homeobox is formed by a 180 bp sequence of DNA (homeobox), which specifies a 60-amino acid sequence that forms a helix-turn-helix structure (homeodomain).

44. List at least three different types of genetic regulation in eukaryotes.

Answer: transcription factors, DNA methylation, gene amplification, posttranscriptional regulation

45. In what way might gene amplification be related to gene regulation? Give an example.

Answer: Gene amplification involves an increase in the number (copies) of genes, which in turn provides the potential for increasing the amount of gene products because more genes are present. Amplification of ribosomal genes during oogenesis in *Xenopus* is an example.

46. In what way is gene rearrangement related to gene regulation? Give an example.

Answer: The reshuffling of genes provides a way for certain gene segments to rearrange to produce new products or change the amounts of gene products. The relative positions of promoters and/or enhancers with respect to structural genes may influence transcription. In the production of immunoglobins, such gene reshuffling occurs.

Sample Questions: Chapter 16 Regulation of Gene Expression

47. Describe the general structure of a transcription factor.

Answer: Transcription factors are modular proteins with at least two functional domains: one binds to DNA in promoters and enhancers, and another activates transcription.

48. List three major structural classifications of DNA-binding domains found in eukaryotic transcription factors.

Answer: helix-turn-helix (HTH), zinc finger, and leucine zipper

49. In what ways are eukaryotic transcription factors thought to function?

Answer: They appear to influence the structural organization of chromatin and possibly looping out of the DNA that separates the enhancer from the transcription initiation complex (transcription factors, promoter, RNA polymerase, etc.)

50. What type of genetic control typically results when transcription factors interact with DNA?

Answer: positive control

51. Approximately 5 % of the cytosine residues are methylated in the genome of any given eukaryote. In what way is DNA methylation related to genetic regulation?

Answer: There is an inverse relationship between the degree of methylation of eukaryotic DNA and the degree of gene expression.

52. Alternative RNA splicing is a method that apparently evolved for the production of many different polypeptides from the same pre-mRNA. Provide an example of alternative splicing.

Answer: Fourteen exons occur in the alpha-tropomyosin gene, six of which make up three pairs that are alternatively spliced. Ten different forms of alpha-tropomyosin are expressed in a tissue-specific manner.

53. Name three different levels of regulation in eukaryotes.

Answer: transcriptional, processing, transport, translational, posttranslational

Sample Questions: Chapter 16   Regulation of Gene Expression

54. Name two consensus sequences or modular DNA sequences that exist upstream from coding regions of some eukaryotic genes.

Answer: TATA, and CAAT sequences

55. In what way is gene expression in eukaryotes influenced by the cellular environment?

Answer: Effector molecules originating outside the cell are transduced by proteins that shuttle from the cytoplasm to the nucleus and regulate transcription.

56. Mutations in the promoter region of the β-globin gene indicate that some areas are more sensitive than others. When mutations occur in consensus sequences (modular elements such as GC box, CAAT box, TATA box), transcription _____.

Answer: decreases

57. Provide a general set of statements thta describe enhancers.

Answer: The position of an enhancer need not be fixed; it can be upstream, downstream, or within the gene it regulates.

58. Describe how nucleosomes may influence gene transcription.

Answer: The binding of transcription factors requires accessing nucleosomal DNA, and such factors may displace nucleosomes.

True/False Format

59. The *lac* operon consists of three structural genes as well as the adjacent region of DNA known as the regulator.

Answer: False

Sample Questions: Chapter 16   Regulation of Gene Expression

60. Regarding the lactose utilization system in *E. coli*, a constitutive mutant is one in which the three enzymes are produced regardless of the presence or absence of lactose.

Answer: True

61. Regarding the lactose utilization system in *E. coli*, a gratuitous inducer is a molecule that is chemically analogous to lactose, induces the operon, but is not a substrate for the enzymes of the *lac* operon.

Answer: True

62. Under a system of negative control, genetic expression occurs unless such expression is shut off by some form of regulator.

Answer: True

63. Under a system of positive control, transcription does not occur unless a regulator molecule directly stimulates RNA production.

Answer: True

64. The enzyme β-galactoside permease cleaves the linkage between glucose and galactose in lactose.

Answer: False

65. The *tryptophan* operon is typically characterized by the following two terms: negative control and repressible.

Answer: True

66. Attenuation is known to occur in the *lactose* operon.

Answer: False

67. Attenuation involves the termination of mRNA synthesis.

Answer: True

68. The *tryptophan* and *lactose* operons both include forms of control that are typically called "negative."

Answer: True

69. Transcription factors are proteins with at least two functional domains, one that binds to DNA and one that binds to RNA polymerase or to other transcription factors.

Answer: True

70. Transcription in eukaryotes is generally influenced by enhancers, just as in prokaryotes.

Answer: False

71. A homeobox is a DNA stretch of 180 bp that specifies a 60-amino-acid homeodomain.

Answer: True

72. In general, one could say that there are fewer levels of regulation possible in prokaryotes than in eukaryotes.

Answer: True

73. The CAAT (CAAT box) sequence appears to be critical to the promoter's ability to facilitate transcription.

Answer: True

74. Regulation of RNA transport through the nuclear membrane is as common in prokaryotes as in eukaryotes.

Answer: False

75. Homeotic genes appear to play a critical role in developmental processes in both prokaryotes and eukaryotes.

Answer: False

76. Alternative RNA processing generates different mRNAs that can direct the synthesis of different polypeptides.

Answer: True

77. Alternative RNA processing can result in different mRNAs that start with different exons.

Answer: True

Sample Questions: Chapter 17 Recombinant DNA Technology

Chapter 17

Multiple Choice Format

1. A polylinker site is composed of a number of unique restriction sites clustered into one region. What process would most likely be related to the use of a polycloning region?

    A.   lysogeny
    B.   reverse transcription
    C.   production of a recombinant plasmid
    D.   conjugation
    E.   deletion

Answer: C

2. Restriction endonucleases are especially useful if they generate sticky ends. What makes an end sticky?

    A.   single-stranded complementary tails
    B.   blunt ends
    C.   poly-A sequences
    D.   5' cap
    E.   interference

Answer: A

3. List two especially useful characteristics of cloning vectors.

    A.   high copy number and antibiotic resistance gene(s)
    B.   virulence and lysogenicity
    C.   ability to integrate into the host chromosome and then cause a lytic cycle
    D.   nonautonomous replication and transposition
    E.   reverse transcriptase and ligase activities

Answer: A

Sample Questions: Chapter 17 Recombinant DNA Technology

4. Some vectors, such as pUC18 and others of the pUC series, contain a large number of restriction enzyme sites clustered in one region. What term is given to this advantageous arrangement of restriction sites?

      A.   palindrome
      B.   consensus sequence
      C.   polylinker
      D.   β-galactosidase
      E.   complementation

Answer: C

5. One of the primary reasons for the necessity of generating a large number in a eukaryotic genomic library is that

      A.   each cosmid replicates nonautomously.
      B.   lysogenic phage continue to integrate their DNA into the host chromosome, thus reducing the number of desired recombinant clones.
      C.   each vector can take up only a relatively small fraction of the eukaryotic DNA.
      D.   each ligation product is sequence specific.
      E.   the host range of the vector is limited.

Answer: C

6. In the context of molecular genetics, reverse translation refers to

      A.   assembling a DNA sequence from an amino acid sequence.
      B.   assembling a RNA sequence from a DNA sequence.
      C.   translating in the 3' to 5' direction.
      D.   transcribing first, then translating.
      E.   making an amino acid sequence from a DNA sequence.

Answer: A

7. Nucleic acid blotting is widely used in recombinant DNA technology. In a Southern blot, one generally

      A.   hybridizes filter-bound DNA with a DNA probe.
      B.   hybridizes filter-bound RNA with a DNA probe.
      C.   examines amino acid substitutions with radioactive probes.
      D.   cleaves RNA with restriction endonucleases.
      E.   cleaves DNA with restriction endonucleases.

Answer: A

Sample Questions: Chapter 17 Recombinant DNA Technology

Short Answer Format

8. What is recombinant DNA technology? What are safety issues related to recombinant DNA technology?

Answer: Recombinant DNA technology refers to the creations of new combinations of DNA molecules that are not normally found in nature. Safety issues generally center around the creation and release (accidental or intentional) of genetically engineered organisms that threaten human health or animals and plants in the environment. Many organisms that are "genetically engineered" carry genes for antibiotic resistance.

9. Nucleic acid blotting is commonly used in molecular biology. Two types, Southern blots and northern blots, involve gel electrophoresis and a filter that holds the nucleic acid. Briefly describe the procedure of "blotting" in this context, and differentiate between Southern and northern blots.

Answer: In a Southern blot the DNA to be "probed" is cut with a restriction enzyme(s), then the fragments are separated by gel electrophoresis. Alkali treatment of the gel denatures the DNA, which is then "blotted" onto the filter (nylon or nitrocellulose). A labeled probe (RNA or DNA) is then hybridized to complementary fragments on the filter. In a northern blot, RNA is separated in the gel and "probed" with the labeled DNA.

10. Assume that you have cut λ DNA with the restriction enzyme *Hin*dIII. You separate the fragments on an agarose gel and stain the DNA with ethidium bromide. You notice that the intensity of the stain is less in the bands that have migrated closer to the "+" pole. Give an explanation for this finding.

Answer: Since the smaller fragments migrate toward the "+" pole, away from the origin, they bind less stain than the larger fragments near the origin.

11. In the context of recombinant DNA technology, what is meant by the term *vector*?

Answer: A vector is a vehicle to carry recombinant DNA molecules into the host cells where independent replication can occur. The most common vectors are plasmids, bacteriophage, and cosmids.

Sample Questions: Chapter 17 Recombinant DNA Technology

12. Molecular biologists rely on many, often sophisticated techniques to pursue their discipline. One may list ultracentrifugation, electron microscopy, X ray diffraction, electrophoresis, and computer interfacing as fundamental. "Organic" or living systems provide the raw materials for study. List four "organisms" (or organismic groups) often used by molecular biologists, and describe a major advantage to the molecular biologist of each.

Answer: Bacteriophage: relatively simple, short generation time. Bacteria: relatively simple, short generation time, simple growth requirements. Yeast: relatively simple for a eukaryote, short generation time, simple growth requirements. *Drosophila*: relatively simple to culture, extensive genetic and developmental information available, "giant" polytene (salivary gland) chromosomes.

13. Assume that a given plasmid vector to be used in a cloning experiment contains 4000 base pairs of DNA. Assume also that the restriction endonuclease *Cuj* cuts this plasmid at the following sites (starting from an arbitraty zero point): 1000, 1500, and 3000. Given complete digestion of the plasmid with the endonuclease so that only linear fragments are produced, what sizes of DNA are expected?

Answer: 500 bp, 1500 bp, 2000 bp

14. Some restriction enzymes cleave DNA in such a manner as to produce blunt ends. Most often the ligation of blunt end fragments is enhanced by the use of the enzyme terminal deoxynucleotidyl transferase. Why?

Answer: Terminal deoxynucleotidyl transferase extends single-stranded ends by the addition of nucleotide tails. If complementary tails are added, the fragments can hybridize and the recombinant molecules can be ligated.

15. Over the years, sophisticated plasmid vectors have been developed for use in recombinant DNA technology. What useful features have been introduced in particular vectors?

Answer: small size to allow large inserts, high copy number, large numbers of unique restriction sites (polylinkers), variety of selection schemes (pigmented colonies, antibiotic resistance)

16. List, in order, the steps usually followed in producing recombinant DNA molecules in a plasmid vector.

Answer: isolation of DNA (foreign and plasmid), digestion of DNAs with an appropriate restriction endonuclease, ligation of fragments, transformation of host cells

Sample Questions: Chapter 17 Recombinant DNA Technology

17. What is a cDNA molecule?

Answer: A cDNA molecule is a DNA copy of an RNA molecule.

18. What is meant by the term *restriction endonuclease* in the context of recombinant DNA technology?

Answer: Isolated from bacteria, restriction endonucleases restrict or prevent viral infection by degrading the invading nucleic acid of the virus.

19. What is meant by the designation *Eco*RI?

Answer: one of the first restriction enzymes isolated from *E. coli*

20. What advantages does pUC18 have in terms of recombinant DNA technology ?

Answer: small size, high copy number, polylinker in *lac*Z gene

21. What term is used to refer to the process in which DNA can be introduced into host bacterial cells?

Answer: transformation (of transfection in some cases)

22. Under ideal conditions, how many copies of all the sequences of the host genome should be represented in a genomic library?

Answer: one

23. What is the specific application of reverse transcriptase in the preparation of cDNA?

Answer: synthesis of DNA to form an RNA-DNA duplex

24. What is the name of the process by which bacterial colonies (cells) are transferred from one agar plate to the another?

Answer: replica plating

Sample Questions: Chapter 17 Recombinant DNA Technology

25. In the polymerase chain reaction, what is the purpose of the initial high temperature? What is the purpose of cooling in the second step?

Answer: denaturing the target (template) DNA, annealing of the primer to the target

26. In what way are specific DNA sequences amplified in the polymerase chain reaction?

Answer: Oligonucleotide primers hydrogen bond to specific sections, and primers are then extended.

27. What is the advantage of having a polylinker region (multiple unique restriction sites) embedded in the *lacZ* component in the pUC series of plasmids?

Answer: An insert of DNA in the polylinker inactivates the *lacZ* component and allows identification of recombinant plasmids under proper genetic and environmental conditions.

28. Assume that one conducted a typical cloning experiment using pUC18, transformed an appropriate host bacterial strain (one carrying the *lacZ* complementing region), and plated the bacteria on an appropriate X-gal medium. Blue and white colonies appeared. Which of the two types of colonies, blue or white, would most likely contain the recombinant pUC18?

Answer: the white colonies, because of insertional activation of the *lacZ* component

29. When conducting a cloning experiment with the lambda phage, would you expect such an experiment to be of more immediate success if the phage entered the lysogenic or if it entered the lytic cycle?

Answer: lytic cycle

30. If one wishes to clone a gene using typical restriction endonucleases, how does the restriction endonuclease recognize genes in the genome?

Answer: Restriction endonucleases don't recognize functional regions in the genome (genes). They can only recognize relatively short DNA sequences that have no relationship to functionality.

Sample Questions: Chapter 17 Recombinant DNA Technology

31. Below are four processes common to most cloning experiments:

> transforming bacteria
> plating bacteria on selective medium
> cutting DNA with restriction endonucleases
> ligating DNA fragments

Place components of the above list in the order in which they would most likely occur during a cloning experiment.

Answer: cutting DNA with restriction endonucleases, ligating DNA fragments, transforming bacteria, plating bacteria on selective medium

True/False Format

32. A common term for a plasmid or other DNA element that serves as a cloning vehicle is vector.

Answer: True

33. Restriction endonucleases recognize palindromic (mirror image) DNA sequences and often generate sticky ends or single-stranded DNA overhangs at cut sites.

Answer: True

34. In general, the main goal of cloning is to include as many different genes as possible in a single cloning vector.

Answer: False

35. The main purpose of a probe is its insertion in plasmid DNA.

Answer: False

36. To isolate a bacterium with a plasmid that carries a desired DNA fragment within the ampicillin resistance gene, we should grow bacteria in a medium that contains ampicillin.

Answer: False

Sample Questions: Chapter 17 Recombinant DNA Technology

37. Restriction endonucleases are capable of producing both blunt and sticky ends.

Answer: True

38. In recombinant DNA technology, a YAC is an enzyme isolated from a large, South American, four-legged mammal.

Answer: False

39. Reverse transcriptase is often used as the heat stable enzyme in PCR.

Answer: False

40. In a typical PCR, primers are used to cleave specific regions of the DNA template.

Answer: False

41. A restriction map provides the location of sites cleaved by restriction enzymes.

Answer: True

42. During a PCR, heat is provided to inactivate the polymerase enzyme.

Answer: False

43. pUC18 is a common YAC.

Answer: False

44. In recombinant DNA technology, a YAC, RFLP, and pUC18 have identical uses.

Answer: False

45. In a PCR, primers are complementary to stretches of DNA with which they anneal.

Answer: True

Sample Questions: Chapter 18 Genomics, Bioinformatics, and Proteomics

Chapter 18

Multiple Choice Format

1. Begun in 1990, the Human Genome Project (HGP) is an international effort to

    A.   construct a physical map of the 3.3 billion base pairs in the human genome.
    B.   collect samples of cells from all parts of the world in order to preserve human genetic diversity.
    C.   collect plant seeds in order to reduce the impact of human activity on plant extinction.
    D.   clone deleterious genes from humans and study their mode of action.
    E.   clone beneficial genes from humans for eventual use in gene therapy.

Answer: A

2. Compared with eukaryotic chromosomes, bacterial chromosomes are

    A.   large, mainly organized in monocistronic transcription units without introns.
    B.   small, mainly organized in monocistronic transcription units with introns.
    C.   large, mainly organized in polycistronic transcription units without introns.
    D.   small, with high gene density.
    E.   large, triple-helix, Z-DNA, organized in monocistronic units with introns.

Answer: D

3. Compared with prokaryotic chromosomes, eukaryotic chromosomes are

    A.   large, mainly organized in monocistronic transcription units without introns.
    B.   small, mainly organized in monocistronic transcription units with introns.
    C.   large, mainly organized in polycistronic transcription units without introns.
    D.   small, mainly organized in polycistronic transcription units without introns.
    E.   large, linear, less densely packed with protein-coding genes, mainly organized in monocistronic units with introns.

Answer: E

Sample Questions: Chapter 18 Genomics, Bioinformatics, and Proteomics

4. Most of the bacterial genomes described in the text have fewer than

    A.   5000 genes.
    B.   5000 base pairs.
    C.   500 genes.
    D.   10,000 base pairs.
    E.   50 genes.

Answer: A

5. A bacterial polycistronic transcription unit is one that

    A.   contains information for one protein product.
    B.   contains information for more than one protein product.
    C.   is capped at the 5'end and carries a poly-A tail at the 3'end.
    D.   is void of start (AUG) and termination (UAA, UGA, UAG) triplets.
    E.   none of the above.

Answer: B

6. When two proteins show a 25% or more match in homology, it is likely that

    A.   the two proteins have identical functions.
    B.   the two proteins have no common origin.
    C.   the two proteins share a common ancestry.
    D.   the two proteins have identical structures.
    E.   the primary structures may differ but the tertiary structures are identical.

Answer: C

7. *Mycoplasma* are among the smallest and perhaps the simplest self-replicating prokaryotes known. *M. genitalium* contains a genome of 0.6 MB. Approximately how many genes does this bacterium contain?

    A.   about 3000
    B.   426,000
    C.   12
    D.   1200
    E.   between 400 and 550

Answer: E

8. Under the umbrella of the HGP (Human Genome Project), scientists are working on the human genome as well as a number of other organisms. Name two additional organisms.

      A   cat and dog
      B.   gorilla and swine
      C.   fruit bat and dog
      D.   yeast and mouse
      E.   mouse and cat

Answer: D

Short Answer Format

9. Name the two main methods that scientists are using to sequence genomes.

Answer: clone-by-clone method and shotgun cloning

10. Give two examples of multigene families.

Answer: A multigene family contains genetic elements which share DNA-sequence homology and descend from a single ancestral gene. Their gene products have similar functions. Two examples are globin genes and immunoglobin genes

11. A number of generalizations can be made about the organization of protein-coding genes in bacterial chromosomes. First, the gene density is very high, averaging about_____.

Answer: one gene per kilobase pair of DNA

12. Archaea (formerly known as Archaebacteria) is one of the three major divisions of living organisms; the other two are Eubacteria and Eukaryotes. While their genome is organized much like eubacteria, some genes more closely resemble those in eukaryotes. Which genes are more eukaryote-like?

Answer: genes involved in RNA synthesis, protein synthesis, and DNA synthesis

13. What appears to the range of number of genes per genome in eukaryotes?

Answer: 5000 to about 40,000

Sample Questions: Chapter 18 Genomics, Bioinformatics, and Proteomics

14. One major difference between a prokaryotic and a eukaryotic gene is that eukaryotic genes contain internal base sequences called_____.

Answer: intervening sequences or introns

15. What is meant by the term *low gene density*? Give an example of an organism with low gene density.

Answer: Low gene density is common in eukaryotes in which there may be as many as 50,000 base pairs containing only six genes as is the case with a segment of human chromosome #7.

16. *Caenorhabditis elegans* is a common inhabitant in the genetics literature. Why?

Answer: Primarily due to the efforts of Sidney Brenner (1960s), who sought a less complex genetic/developmental model than *Drosophila*, *C. elegans* has found favor because it contains a fixed number of cells, a fixed cellular lineage, and a relatively small genome (about 20,000 protein-coding genes in 97 Mb).

17. What surprising finding has come from sequencing portions of the *C. elegans* genome in terms of gene structure?

Answer: Approximately 25% of the genes are organized into polycistronic transcription units like those of bacteria.

18. Present an overview of the gene organization in large-genome plants.

Answer: Large-genome plants are characterized by having very small islands of unique sequence DNA containing a gene or two separated from other islands by large blocks of transposable elements (TEs).

19. Describe the relationship between introns and organismic complexity in eukaryotes.

Answer: Going from yeast to multicellular eukaryotes, the proportion of genes with introns increases, the number of introns per gene increases, and the sizes of the introns increase.

Sample Questions: Chapter 18 Genomics, Bioinformatics, and Proteomics

20. Multiple proteins that arise from single-gene duplications are known as *paralogs*. Give an example of a human gene family that is likely to arise from such duplications.

Answer: The hemoglobin gene family encodes various polypeptides that are part of hemoglobin molecules, and exemplify a multigene family that arose by duplication and dispersal into different chromosomes.

21. List three mechanisms known to produce gene duplications.

Answer: unequal crossing over, unequal sister chromatid exchange, replication errors

22. What is meant by the term *pseudogene*? Give an example.

Answer: Pseudogenes are nonfunctional versions of genes that resemble other gene sequences but contain significant nucleotide substitutions, deletions, and duplications that prevent their expression. Pseudogenes are designated by the prefix ψ (psi).

23. Present a general definition for a *multigene family*.

Answer: Multigene families share DNA sequence homology and their gene products are functionally related. They are often (but not always) found together in a single location in a chromosome.

24. Describe the organization of the α-globin gene in humans.

Answer: The alpha-group spans more than 30 kb and contains three genes; *zeta*, and two copies of the *alpha* gene. In addition, two nonfunctional pseudogenes are in the group. Most of the DNA in this region consists of intergenic spacer DNA.

25. One of the dominant features of the immune system is the capacity to generate new cells that contain different combinations of antibodies. Because there are billions of such combinations, it is impossible that each combination is coded by a separate gene. How is such diversity accomplished?

Answer: Four special features are known to account for immunoglobin diversity: (1) multiple numbers of variable regions, (2) multiple numbers of diversity and joining regions, (3) multiple splice locations with break-nibble-add joining, and (4) multiple combination of light chains with heavy chains.

26. How are pseudogenes formed?

Answer: probably through point mutations, deletions, and duplications -- any sequence that renders the gene nonfunctional

27. Briefly describe general trends relating to DNA content and gene number in major groups of organisms.

Answer: Eukaryotes contain more DNA in their genomes than bacteria and exhibit a wide variation of DNA amount among different groups. Evolutionary expansion has been accompanied by increased amounts of DNA, with more "complex" forms containing more DNA than less complex forms. Such change in DNA content is not universally accompanied by increases in gene number. Some closely related species may vary more than tenfold in their DNA content.

True/False Format

28. The genomic organization of all living creatures is identical.

Answer: False

29. The terms *proteomics* and *genomics* mean essentially the same thing.

Answer: False

30. The Human Genome Project is an international effort to construct a physical map sequence of the 3.3 billion base pairs in the haploid human genome.

Answer: True

31. Typically, less than 1% of bacterial DNA is noncoding repetitive sequence DNA.

Answer: True

32. Introns are found only in prokaryotic genomes.

Answer: False

Sample Questions: Chapter 18 Genomics, Bioinformatics, and Proteomics

33. Genes of Archaea are almost identical to eukaryotic genes in terms of structure.

Answer: False

34. It appears as if about 5000 functional genes is the minimum genome size necessary for life.

Answer: False

35. Humans have more DNA than any other organism.

Answer: False

36. There is a general inverse relationship between DNA content and organismic complexity.

Answer: False

37. Bacterial genes have introns, eukaryotic genes lack introns.

Answer: False

38. In humans, no genes are larger than 2 kb.

Answer: False

39. Multigene families are characterized by clusters of tandemly arranged unique pseudogenes organized as operons.

Answer: False

Chapter 19

Multiple Choice Format

1. RFLPs and minisatellites are commonly used in recombinant DNA technology to

     A.   cleave DNA of interest.
     B.   generate pharmaceutical products of interest.
     C.   serve as recombinant DNA vectors.
     D.   map genes and DNA fingerprints.
     E.   substitute for oligonucleotides.

Answer: D

2. VNTRs are sections of DNA with the following characteristics:

     A.   variable amino acid substitutions, highly heterogeneous.
     B.   variable numbers of tandem repeats, highly uniform in the population.
     C.   variable numbers of tandem repeats, variable in the population.
     D.   various nucleotides transcribed repeatedly, homogeneous.
     E.   very noteworthy transcribed regions, lethal genes.

Answer: C

3. Beta thalassemia is an autosomal recessive disorder caused by which of the following?

     A.   decreased or absent *alpha* chain production
     B.   deletion of bases in the *gamma* hemoglobin chain
     C.   decreased or absence of *beta* chain of hemoglobin
     D.   overproduction of the *beta* chain of hemoglobin
     E.   premature cleavage of the *beta* chain of hemoglobin

Answer: C

Sample Questions: Chapter 19 Biotechnology and Its Implications for Society

4. RFLPs are commonly used in gene mapping as

- A. *in situ* hybridization probes.
- B. supplements for restriction endonucleases.
- C. genetic markers.
- D. primers for PCR.
- E. substitutes for VNTRs in gene therapy.

Answer: C

5. The ratio of two probabilities (no linkage/certain degree of linkage) is expressed as the odds for a degree of linkage. The computations are known as *logarithm of the odds* or *lod* score. What *lod* score is taken as evidence of linkage between two markers?

- A. 3 or greater
- B. 2 or less
- C. 1, 2
- D. 3 only
- E. 2.5 and below

Answer: A

6. An exclusion map refers to

- A. individuals who are not part of the linkage study.
- B. genes that are not involved in the trait in question.
- C. chromosomes and/or chromosome regions where a gene in question is not located.
- D. the Y chromosome, that in humans is virtually void of typical genes.
- E. RFLP markers which are excluded from the study.

Answer: C

7. Under strictly controlled conditions, a probe can be used that will hybridize only with its complementary sequence and not with other sequences that may vary by as little as one nucleotide. What are such probes called?

- A. mutation-specific probes
- B. short, variable repeats
- C. VNTRs
- D. microsatellites
- E. allele-specific oligonucleotides (ASOs)

Answer: E

Sample Questions: Chapter 19 Biotechnology and Its Implications for Society

Short Answer Format

8. Alleles that differ by as little as a single nucleotide can be distinguished by synthetic probes known as _____.

Answer: allele-specific oligonucleotides (ASO).

9. The transfer of genes into somatic cells is called _____, whereas the transfer of genes into the germ line is called _____; _____ is a form of therapy in which human potential can be enhanced for some desired trait.

Answer: somatic gene therapy, germ-line therapy, enhancement gene therapy

10. List the steps likely to be used in sequencing the human genome (the Human Genome Project).

Answer: construction of a high-resolution genetic map related to RFLP or other markers, construction of physical maps, sequencing, interpretation

11. Prenatal detection of human diseases has been greatly enhanced by two procedures. Name and briefly describe each.

Answer: *Amniocentesis* is the withdrawal of amniotic fluid by a needle inserted through the mother's abdomen and *chorionic villus sampling* is the use of a catheter to sample the fetal chorion.

12. Briefly define what is meant by *gene therapy*.

Answer: Gene therapy transfers a normal allele into a somatic cell that carries one or more mutant alleles.

13. The first person to receive gene therapy was a young girl with adenosine deaminase (ADA) deficiency. Outline the therapeutic steps involved.

Answer: isolation of T cells, mixing T cells with virus containing the normal human ADA gene, infection of T cells with a virus, growth of modified T cells in the laboratory, reintroduction of modified T cells into patient

Sample Questions: Chapter 19 Biotechnology and Its Implications for Society

14. List the general guidelines for gene therapy.

Answer: gene must be available for cloning, there must be an effective means of transferring the gene, target tissue must be accessible, no other effective therapy available

15. What is a fusion polypeptide?

Answer: a functional protein composed of two polypeptide chains

16. What is a transcriptome? What is a proteome?

Answer: A transcriptome is the set of mRNA molecules produced by a cell at any given time. A proteome is the expressed set of proteins present in a cell at any given time.

17. Briefly describe what is meant by the term *edible vaccine*.

Answer: Using recombinant DNA technology, viral surface proteins can be spliced into edible plants with the goal of plant leaves and fruit serving as a source of oral vaccines.

18. How are gene therapy and recombinant DNA technology related?

Answer: Gene therapy refers to the application of recombinant DNA technology to treat inherited disorders by replacing defective genes with copies of normal alleles.

19. Describe a DNA microarray and its use.

Answer: A DNA microarray is a glass plate divided into fields containing a specific DNA probe of about 20 nucleotides. The sequence of the probe differs by one nucleotide from field to field. A chip can hold more than 500,000 fields. DNA is extracted from cells and cut with one or more restriction enzymes. The fragments are fluorescence tagged, denatured, and annealed to the DNA in the array. Massive amounts of DNA can be screened for sequence changes in a relatively short period of time.

20. Describe a minisatellite section of DNA.

Answer: areas of tandem repeat sequences

Sample Questions: Chapter 19 Biotechnology and Its Implications for Society

21. The first attempts at gene therapy began in 1990, the treatment of a young girl with a genetic disorder abbreviated SCID. What does SCID stand for? What does ADA stand for?

Answer: Severe Combined Immunodeficiency and Adenosine DeAminase

22. Generally, vaccines are used to stimulate the immune system by providing antigens of potential pathogens. What does one often receive in a vaccine?

Answer: inactivated or attenuated viruses

23. A term often used to describe an organism that is a genetic mosaic is

Answer: transgenic.

24. DNA fingerprinting often makes use of VNTRs. Why?

Answer: VNTRs (variable number tandem repeats) are highly variable portions of eukaryotic chromosomes. They are sufficiently variable to be unique to each individual.

25. What is an allele-specific oligonucleotide?

Answer: An allele-specific oligonucleotide is a stretch of DNA capable of either base pairing with a specific allele or failing to do so. Either way, such oligonucleotides can be used, under stringent hybridization conditions, to detect minor differences in DNA sequences.

26. Briefly describe how a Southern blot is prepared and its uses.

Answer: A Southern blot is designed to literally "blot" electrophoresed DNA from a gel onto a supporting medium, usually nitrocellulose or nylon. The medium is placed directly on the gel and a transfer buffer is drawn through the gel carrying the DNA to the medium. Once the medium is dried and the DNA denatured, it can be "probed" to determine the location and amount of complementary DNA. Southern blots are used to identify particular DNA locations and amounts often from complex mixtures of DNA fragments.

27. Vaccines can be used to stimulate the immune system to prevent certain diseases. Vaccines are often _____ and _____ viruses.

Answer: inactivated, attenuated

28. Provide several uses for examining sequence variants such as RFLPs and VNTRs.

Answer: forensic applications, paternity testing, archeology, conservation biology, public health, evolutionary biology

True/False Format

29. A restriction fragment is generated by the action of a restriction enzyme (endonuclease).

Answer: True

30. Glyphosate (a herbicide) inhibits EPSP, a chloroplast enzyme involved in the synthesis of several amino acids.

Answer: True

31. To generate glyphosate resistance in crop plants, a fusion gene was created that introduced a viral promoter to control the EPSP synthetase gene.

Answer: True

32. One of the problems associated with the generation of transgenic plants is that ecological parameters of many plants are not completely understood.

Answer: True

33. *Drosophila* is a unique candidate for genetic engineering because it is the one prokaryote about which we have a great deal of genetic information.

Answer: False

34. *Drosophila* contains a number of transposable genetic elements including P elements, which allow genetic markers to be inserted into the genome.

Answer: True

35. Amniocentesis is preferred over chorionic villus sampling because recombinant DNA screening can be achieved with amniocentesis but not chorionic villus sampling.

Answer: False

36. Gene therapy will probably be used predominantly for correcting germ line mutations because there are fewer ethical issues compared with somatic cell gene therapy.

Answer: False

37. Biotechnology has yet to produce a single useful product for a human health condition.

Answer: False

38. The Human Genome Project seeks to rid the human population of genetic disease.

Answer: False

39. It is likely that new methods of delivering vaccines will be developed so that traditional injection will be less frequent.

Answer: True

Chapter 20

Multiple Choice Format

1. What term refers to the regulatory events that establish a specific pattern of gene activity and developmental fate for a given cell?

        A.   lysogen
        B.   differentiation
        C.   determination
        D.   gradient regulated
        E.   attenuation

Answer: C

2. What general genetic process is believed to account for the variety of cellular structures and functions in eukaryotic cells?

        A.   variable gene activity
        B.   negative control exclusively
        C.   maternal environmental activities
        D.   intron processing
        E.   RNA processing

Answer: A

3. Immediately after fertilization of a *Drosophila* egg, the zygote nucleus undergoes a series of divisions. Subsequent nuclear migration generates a

        A.   syncytial blastoderm.
        B.   maternal effect.
        C.   homeodomain.
        D.   zygote.
        E.   cleavage nucleus.

Answer: A

Sample Questions: Chapter 20 Genes and Development

4. Development appears to occur as a result of successive subdivisions of anatomical/functional domains. Segments are formed in some embryos, and each segment is determined to form either anterior or posterior regions. What term is often applied to such regions?

      A.   segmental fracture
      B.   gap faction
      C.   compartment
      D.   homeodomain
      E.   transdetermined aspect

Answer: C

5. In *Drosophila*, segmentation genes function in a sequential manner in the following order:

      A.   gap, segment-polarity, pair-rule
      B.   pair-rule, transdeterminal, gap
      C.   transdeterminal, gap, pair-rule
      D.   gap, pair-rule, segment-polarity
      E.   segmentational, helical, spherical

Answer: D

6. Anterior/posterior regions of insect segments undergo progressive restrictions during development. These regions are known as

      A.   homeodomains.
      B.   segmental fractions.
      C.   fate domains.
      D.   blastoderms.
      E.   compartments.

Answer: E

7. Mutations that produce large gaps in the *Drosophila* embryo's segmentation pattern are called

      A.   homeodomains.
      B.   gap genes.
      C.   compartment genes.
      D.   linkage genes.
      E.   segment genes.

Answer: B

Sample Questions: Chapter 20 Genes and Development

Short Answer Format

8.   Explain the differences between *differentiation* and *determination*. Provide examples of each process, and indicate how each is involved in development.

Answer: Determination is the early commitment of a cell to an eventual developmental fate. Differentiation is the set of functional and structural changes associated with the expression of that developmental fate. When nuclei of the developing *Drosophila* embryo reach the blastoderm stage, they become determined. Differentiation of the cells of the imaginal disks in *Drosophila* occurs during metamorphosis. Development, therefore, probably depends first on the determination of cells, then on the differentiation of cells.

9.   How does determination relate to differentiation?

Answer: Determination occurs when a cell's developmental fate is set, whereas differentiation is the expression of that determined state. Determination occurs before differentiation.

10.   Define the following terms:

   determination
   differentiation

Answer: Determination is the early commitment of a cell to an eventual developmental fate. Differentiationis the set of functional and structural changes associated with the expression of that developmental fate.

11. Maternal effects are cases of extrachromosomal inheritance where the genotype of the mother influences the phenotype of her immediate offspring in a non-Mendelian manner. Provide a rationale for the molecular basis of a maternal effect.

Answer: During development of the egg, females provide numerous nutritional and informational substances that direct and support early embryonic development. These substances are often in the form of transcription factors, receptors, mRNA, and proteins, although other substances are also likely (substrates and products). In some cases, these maternally supplied substances override the actual genotype of the zygote and produce a *phenotype* much like the *genotype* of the mother.

Sample Questions: Chapter 20   Genes and Development

12. Provide a brief description of the variable gene activity hypothesis as it relates to development. What information is often provided in support of this hypothesis?

Answer: Since all cells apparently have the same genetic information yet may differ structurally and functionally, the variable gene activity hypothesis suggests that differential gene transcription (genetic regulation) accounts for such cellular diversity. Evidence in support of this model includes the following: chromosome puffs, isozymes, and the presence of genes but no gene products in some tissues (hemoglobin, for example).

13.   What experiments support the notion of genomic equivalence in regard to development in multicellular organisms? Design an experiment that would allow you to determine if a particular nucleus in a *Drosophila* embryo is capable of directing development of a new *Drosophila*.

Answer: Experiments in support of genomic equivalence include the following: the observation that chromosome number and structure do not consistently change in different cells of an organism, nuclear transplantation in amphibians, and the presence of genes but no gene products in some tissues (hemoglobin, for example).   The recent cloning of Dolly supports the above also. For the *Drosophila* experiment, one could do nuclear transplantation similar to the classic experiments in amphibians and recent experiments in mammals.

14.   Experiments involving nuclear transplantation in amphibians indicate that nuclei derived from blastula are more likely to support development of complete and normal adults compared with those derived from later stages of development. Do these findings argue against the current thinking of genomic equivalence in differentiated cells?

Answer: By serial transfers of nuclei from differentiated cells, Gurdon found that such "later" nuclei can also direct complete development of the tadpole, thus indicating that all genes are present in differentiated nuclei.

15. Which functions earlier in development, maternal effect genes or zygotic genes?

Answer: maternal effect genes

Sample Questions: Chapter 20   Genes and Development

16. Describe the anatomy and function of insect imaginal disks.

Answer: The adult body of *Drosophila* derives from small sacks of cells called imaginal disks, which develop in larval stages. There are 12 bilaterally paired disks, each being a major contributor to an adult structure (eye, wing, *etc.*).

17. Genes which specify the fate of each anatomical segment in *Drosophila* are called_____.

Answer: selector genes

18. In *Drosophila*, segmentation genes function in what sequential manner?

Answer: gap, pair-rule, segment-polarity

19. What is the general order of genes involved in determining early *Drosophila* development?

Answer: saternal effect, gap, pair-rule, segment-polarity, selector (homeotic)

20. After segment boundaries are established by the action of the segmentation genes, which specific set of genes appears to be activated?

Answer: selector genes

21. Mutations in the selector genes sometimes form structures in the wrong segment, transforming the antenna of a fly into a leg for example. What term is given to such mutations?

Answer: someotic

22. Give a brief definition of a *homeobox*.

Answer: A homeobox is a highly conserved genetic element which encodes a 60 amino acid sequence with DNA-binding characteristics

Sample Questions: Chapter 20 Genes and Development

23. It is often said that development is a two-step process. What two steps are likely to be referred to here?

Answer: determination and differentiation

24. Experiments carried out in a variety of organisms indicate that the determined state is not fixed. What experiments support this indication?

Answer: nuclear transplantation in a variety of organisms including frogs and mammals (Dolly)

25. What kinds of general observations cause one to conclude that development is the result of variable gene activity?

Answer: Individual cells of multicellular organisms produce different gene products and each apparently has an equal genomic complement.

26. One of the strongest lines of evidence that specialized cells of an adult carries all the genetic information for an entire adult organism comes from what types of experiments?

Answer: nuclear transplantation

27. One advantage of working with *Drosophila* as an experimental organism is the presence of groups of cells set aside early in development to form the adult organism. What are these groups of cells called?

Answer: imaginal disks

28. The *bicoid* gene of *Drosophila* generates embryos with two posterior regions. What general gradient is influenced by the *bicoid* gene?

Answer: anterior-posterior polarity

29. It is currently believed that the distribution of substances in the egg, positioned by the mother, is responsible for establishing the determined state. What general term is used in describing such molecular positioning?

Answer: internal molecular gradients

Sample Questions: Chapter 20   Genes and Development

30.   What is the significance of the homeodomain?

Answer: The homeodomain is a highly conserved protein of 60 amino acids found in a variety of organisms, which, in conjunction with other factors (POU domains) are thought to play a role in DNA binding and transcriptional activation.

31. Molecular/structural orientations (gradients) in an egg are thought to play a significant role in development. What is the origin of such gradients? What evidence indicates that the maternal genotype is involved in providing such gradients?

Answer: In examples of maternal effects, the mother's genotype establishes the early body plan. During formation of any egg, nutritional, regulatory, and informational molecules (RNAs) are placed in appropriate positions for development of the embryo. In *Drosophila* many maternal effect genes have been identified.

32. Describe the relationship between the maternal effect gene *bicoid* and the zygotic gene *hunchback*.

Answer: The bicoid protein is a transcription factor that binds to a series of consequences in the upstream promoter of *hunchback*. Such binding activates the expression of *hunchback*.

33. Three investigators, Nusslein-Volhard, Wieshaus, and Lewis won the Nobel Prize for Physiology or Medicine in 1995 for work they did in the 1970 with *Drosophila*. Briefly describe their findings.

Answer: They identified and characterized a number of maternal effect and zygotic genes that control embryogenesis in *Drosophila*.

34. Provide a brief description of *segment polarity genes*.

Answer: Segment polarity genes are controlled by transcription factors encoded by the pair-rule genes. Expression of these genes divide the embryo into 14 segments and the gene products control the cellular identity within each segment.

True/False Format

35. In *Drosophila*, maternal effect genes are influential in determining the anterior-posterior organization of the developing embryo.

Answer: True

36. Segmentation genes, such as the pair-rule class, are inherited through mitochondrial DNA in *Drosophila*.

Answer: False

37. A *homeobox* gene is one that produces a group of repetitive base sequences such as a VNTR.

Answer: False

38. *Caenorhabditis elegans* is extremely useful as an experimental organism because it has relatively few cells and, for the most part, each embryonic cell's fate is developmentally fixed.

Answer: True

39. Maternally derived molecular gradients appear to determine the anterior-posterior axis in *Drosophila*.

Answer: True

40. *Determination* is the process whereby a cell's eventual developmental fate is set.

Answer: True

41. *Differentiation* is the process whereby a cell's determined state is expressed.

Answer: True

42. Genetic involvement in development appears to be achieved, at least in part, by variable gene activity.

Answer: True

Chapter 21

Multiple Choice Format

1. Mutations in genes that are normally involved in promoting the cell cycle are known as

      A.   tumor suppressors.
      B.   proto-oncogenes.
      C.   oncogenes.
      D.   malignant genes.
      E.   attenuators.

Answer: C

2. What is the name of the protein that combines with cyclins to exert local control of the cell cycle?

      A.   cyclin-dependent kinase
      B.   phosphatase
      C.   ATPase
      D.   integrase
      E.   hexokinase

Answer: A

3. Approximately what percentage of breast cancers are believed to be genetically predisposed, that is, are inherited?

      A.   40%
      B.   60%
      C.   100%
      D.   10%
      E.   90%

Answer: A

Sample Questions: Chapter 21 The Genetic Basis of Cancer

4. Concerning sporadic cases of retinoblastoma, how many gene mutations are thought to be necessary in the same cell for a tumor to develop?

A.   one
B.   four
C.   two
D.   six
E.   insufficient information to answer this question

Answer: C

5. What is the name of the protein that appears to regulate the entry of cells into an S phase? This protein is also known as the "guardian of the genome."

A.   p34
B.   p102
C.   cyclin
D.   p53
E.   phosphokinase

Answer: D

6. A protein that functions as a cell cycle regulator causes cell death (apoptosis) under high sunlight exposure. What is the symbol given this protein?

A.   p34
B.   p102
C.   cyclin
D.   p53
E.   phosphokinase

Answer: D

7. Three general mechanisms appear to be involved in the conversion of proto-oncogenes to oncogenes:

A.   point mutations, translocations, overexpression.
B.   inversions, translocations, methylation.
C.   familial, sporadic, phosphorylation.
D.   transdetermination, mutation, allosteric interactions.
E.   suppression, tabulation, projection.

Answer: A

Sample Questions: Chapter 21 The Genetic Basis of Cancer
Short Answer Format

8. Provide a definition of cancer at the genetic level.

Answer: Cancer is a genetic disorder that can result from the mutation of a given gene or genes, which may produce a defective gene product or a change in the timing or amount of gene expression. Such mutations alter cell cycle control.   Some cancers show familial distributions.

9. Provide a definition of cancer at the anatomical level.

Answer: Cancer is the uncontrolled proliferation of cells and the ability of cells to metastasize or migrate to other sites to form secondary growths.

10. Describe the general relationship that may exist between mutations and cancer.

Answer: Control of the cell cycle is dependent on a variety of gene-produced proteins, such as kinases, cyclins, and related factors. Mutations in genes that encode these proteins may disrupt normal cell cycle control. The G1 checkpoint is altered in some forms of cancer, and mutant cyclins have been shown to be related to a gene product that is overexpressed in some forms of leukemia. Nonmutant genes often suppress the formation of cancer by exerting control over the cell cycle. When mutant, such control may be lost.

11. Describe two classes of proteins known to be involved in regulation of the cell cycle.

Answer: Protein kinases selectively phosphorylate target proteins. When complexed with cyclins, critical points of the cell cycle are controlled.

12. Describe the major events that mark the entry of mitosis from G2.

Answer: condensation of chromatin to form chromosomes, breakdown of the nuclear membrane, alterations in the cytoskeleton, formation of an active CDK1/cyclin B complex

13. What is retinoblastoma, and what is its supposed genetic basis?

Answer: Retinoblastoma is cancer of the retinal cells of the eye. A familial form is known (about 40% of all cases), which is caused by a dominant gene. It occurs in a frequency of about 1/17,000, usually appearing at 1 to 3 years of age. A second form of retinoblastoma is not familial (60% of all cases), develops later in life, and usually only involves one eye. Two mutations are thought to be required for the disease to occur.

Sample Questions: Chapter 21   The Genetic Basis of Cancer

14. What is a tumor suppressor gene? What are oncogenes? What is the normal (nonmutant) cellular version of an oncogene called?

Answer: A tumor suppressor gene is a gene whose normal function is to suppress cell division. When mutant, cell division control is lost and a cancer may form. Oncogenes are genes that induce or maintain uncontrolled cellular proliferation associated with cancer. The normal cellular version of an oncogene is called a proto-oncogene.

15. Describe the function of the *ras* gene family.

Answer: The *ras* gene family encodes a protein consisting of 189 amino acids, that is involved with signal transduction in the cell membrane. Point mutations may cause changes in function to allow signals to enter the cell abnormally, thus stimulating uncontrolled cell growth.

16. Describe three separate mechanisms whereby proto-oncogenes are associated with overexpression.

Answer: They may acquire a new promoter, upstream regulatory signals, or additional copies (amplification).

17. Chronic myelogenous leukemia appears to be associated with a chromosomal rearrangement. How is a chromosomal rearrangement responsible for this disease?

Answer: The joining of chromosomes #9 and #22 through translocation generates a hybrid gene *bcr/c-abl* which produces a 200 kDa protein that is implicated in causing the disease.

18. What is the genus name of the eukaryotic organism that has provided our fundamental knowledge of the nature of cell cycle control?

Answer: *Saccharomyces, Schizosaccharomyces*

19.   What is the name of a normal gene that promotes cellular division?

Answer: proto-oncogene

20. List three general categories of genetic changes that lead to the formation of oncogenes.

Answer: point mutations, translocations, overexpression

21. What is the difference between a *tumor suppressor gene* and a *proto-oncogene*?

Answer: Tumor suppressor genes act to restrict cell division, while proto-oncogenes act to stimulate cell division.

Sample Questions: Chapter 21   The Genetic Basis of Cancer

22. When someone has a predisposition to cancer, what genetic circumstance likely exists?

Answer: The person inherited a germ line mutation.

23. Describe the nature of mutation, as related to cancer, in a *ras* gene.

Answer: The *ras* gene family encodes a protein of 189 amino acids which is involved with signal transduction in the cell membrane. Point mutations may cause changes in function to allow signals to enter the cell abnormally, thus stimulating uncontrolled cell growth.

24. What three stages in the cell cycle seem to serve as points of control (checkpoints)?

Answer: G1/S, and G2/M, M

25. Chronic myelocytic leukemia appears to be associated with a chromosomal rearrangement. What chromosome(s) is (are) involved, and what is the name of the rearrangement?

Answer: Chromosomes #9 and #22 are involved in a translocation.

26. Why do cancer researchers study molecular events associated with mitosis?

Answer: While mitosis is a basic process related to genetic and general biological studies, it is also a significant event in the cell cycle. The cell cycle is regulated by a variety of gene products, which, when altered by mutation may lead to cancer.

27. What is the significance of the CDKs?

Answer: CDK symbolizes a class of protein kinases which, when activated, selectively phosphorylate target proteins. Many of these phosphorylated proteins are involved in cell cycle control.

28. What functional differences exist between various cyclins?

Answer: Cyclins combine with a kinase to regulate the initiation of DNA synthesis (S phase) and the G2/mitosis transition. Different cyclins appear to play a role in differentiating precise actions.

29. Name three human cancers with a genetic predisposition. What appears to be the genetic status of each?

Answer: retinoblastoma (RB): autosomal dominant with 90% penetrance; breast cancer: mutations in *BRCA1* and *BRCA2*;   FAP-associated colon cancer: mutations in *APC*, *DCC*, and *p53* are involved

Sample Questions: Chapter 21   The Genetic Basis of Cancer

30. Differentiate among the following types of genes: *tumor suppressor gene*, *proto-oncogene*, *oncogene*.

Answer: Tumor suppressor genes normally function to inactivate or repress cell division. Proto-oncogenes normally function to promote cell division, while oncogenes are mutant forms of proto-oncogenes.

31. Describe three distinct mechanisms in which proto-oncogene activation is associated with overexpression.

Answer: acquisition of a new promoter, acquisition of a new enhancer, amplification

32. Much has been written lately about *p53* in terms of cancer biology. What is *p53* and what is its significance?

Answer: Mutations in the *p53* gene are important in the development of a number of cancers. It is a tumor suppressor gene that normally functions to control the transition from late G1 to S phase. The product of *p53* has DNA-binding properties.

33. List several classes of environmental agents that are known to cause cancer.

Answer: radiation, chemicals, sunlight, diet, tobacco

34. Name two of the classes of proteins which combine to directly control progression through the cell cycle.

Answer: protein kinases, cyclins

35. What two properties are shared by various types of cancer cells.

Answer: uncontrolled cell duplication, metastasis

36. Provide a simple definition for a *carcinogen*.

Answer: a cancer-causing agent

37. The genetic difference between familial retinoblastoma and sporadic retinoblastoma appears to be based on those with the familial form starting out being _____, while those with the sporadic form starting out being _____.

Answer: heterozygous for the *retinoblastoma* gene, homozygous normal

38. The familial form of retinoblastoma is characterized by cancer appearing in both eyes relatively early in life. In contrast, the sporadic form is usually unilateral and later appearing. Why the difference?

Answer: Individuals with the familial form inherited one *retinoblastoma* mutation.

True/False Format

39. As more is learned about cancer it has become clear that cancer, with few exceptions, has no genetic basis.

Answer: False

40. The gene *p53* is called the "guardian of the genome" because it corrects mutations in the spindle apparatus before nondisjunction can occur.

Answer: False

41. The genome of humans is remarkably stable, so much so that there are no cancers known to result from genomic instability.

Answer: False

42. There are several checkpoints in the mitotic cell cycle. All occur in the S phase.

Answer: False

43. A retrovirus uses reverse transcriptase to make a DNA copy of RNA.

Answer: True

44. There are two types of retinoblastoma, *familial* and *sporadic*. In the familial form, generally one inherits a defective gene from one parent.

Answer: True

45. A *tumor suppressor gene* normally functions to suppress cell division.

Answer: True

46. Any agent that causes damage to DNA is a potential carcinogenic.

Answer: True

47. When the normal retinoblastoma protein is dephosphorylated, it acts to suppress cell division by binding to and inactivating the E2F transcription factor.

Answer: True

Sample Questions: Chapter 22 Population Genetics

Chapter 22

Multiple Choice Format

1. Name the two individuals who provided the foundation for the modern interpretation of evolution.

        A.   Beadle and Tatum
        B.   Watson and Crick
        C.   Darwin and Wallace
        D.   Franklin and Wilkins
        E.   Creighton and McClintock

Answer: C

2. Consanguineous marriages often lead to

        A.   inbreeding.
        B.   gene pools.
        C.   sibling species.
        D.   an increase in heterozygosity as a rule.
        E.   hybrid vigor.

Answer: A

3. What term is given to the genetic information carried by all members of a population?

        A.   gene pool
        B.   genome
        C.   chromosome complement
        D.   breeding unit
        E.   race

Answer: A

Sample Questions: Chapter 22 Population Genetics

4. In a population of 100 individuals, 49% are of the *NN* blood type. What percentage is expected to be *MN* assuming Hardy-Weinberg equilibrium conditions?

    A.   9%
    B.   21%
    C.   42%
    D.   51%
    E.   insufficient information to answer this question

Answer: C

5. Albinism is an autosomal recessive trait in humans. Assume that there are 100 albinos (*aa*) in a population of 1 million. How many individuals would be expected to be homozygous normal (*AA*) under equilibrium conditions?

    A.   19,800
    B.   100
    C.   980,100
    D.   999,900
    E.   10,000

Answer: C

6. In small isolated populations, gene frequencies can fluctuate considerably. The term that applies to this circumstance is

    A.   genetic isolation.
    B.   allelic separation.
    C.   natural selection.
    D.   stabilizing selection.
    E.   genetic drift.

Answer: E

7. The discipline within evolutionary biology that studies changes in allele frequencies is known as

    A.   population genetics.
    B.   consanguineous.
    C.   hybrid vigor.
    D.   genetics.
    E.   cytogenetics.

Answer: A

Sample Questions: Chapter 22 Population Genetics

Short Answer Format

8.   Assume that a trait is caused by the homozygous (or hemizygous) state of a gene that is recessive and X-linked. Nine percent of the females in a given population express the phenotype caused by this gene. What percentage of males would be expected to express this trait? What percentage of the females would be heterozygous for the gene?

Answer: 30% of the males would express the trait. 42% of the females would be heterozygous.

9.   In a population that meets the Hardy-Weinberg equilibrium assumptions, 81 % of the individuals are homozygous for a recessive gene. What percentage of the individuals would be expected to be heterozygous for this gene in the next generation?

Answer: 18%

10.   In a population of cattle, the following color distribution was noted: 36% red (*RR*), 48% roan (*Rr*), and 16% (*rr*). Is this population in a Hardy-Weinberg equilibrium? What will be the distribution of genotypes in the next generation if the Hardy-Weinberg assumptions are met?

Answer: Yes, it is in equilibrium. The distribution will be the same in the next generation.

11.   List factors that change gene frequencies in populations.

Answer: mutation, migration, selection, genetic drift

12.   List and briefly describe factors that contribute to the phenomenon of natural selection.

Answer: variation among members of a species, overpopulation, and competition for mates and survival

13.   List and briefly describe the assumptions that pertain under a population in a Hardy-Weinberg equilibrium.

Answer: infinitely large population, random mating, no selective advantage of one genotype, no migration, mutation, or genetic drift

Sample Questions: Chapter 22 Population Genetics

14. Assume that in a Hardy-Weinberg population, 9% of the individuals are of the homozygous recessive phenotype. What percentage of the individuals would be expected to be heterozygous? What percentage homozygous dominant?

Answer: 42% heterozygous, 49% homozygous dominant

15. Define the term *fitness* and relate it to the meaning of *selection coefficient*.

Answer: Fitness is the probability that a particular phenotype will produce offspring while the selection coefficient is the mathematical difference between the fitness of a given genotype and the optimal fitness for a given genotype.

16. A classic example of selection in natural populations involves the peppered moth *Biston betularia,* in England. Industrial gases killed the lichens and mosses on buildings, trees, etc. and soot deposited on the landscape. Dark-colored moths gained a selective advantage. In this case, one would say that there was selection against the light-colored moths. Which morph, light or dark, would have the highest fitness?

Answer: the dark morph

17. Contrast *directional* and *stabilizing* forms of selection.

Answer: In directional selection, a particular phenotypic extreme is selected for, while in stabilizing selection, both extreme phenotypes are selected against.

18. In a population of 10,000 individuals, where 3600 are *MM*, 1600 are *NN*, and 4800 are *MN*, what are the frequencies of the *M* alleles and *N* alleles?

Answer: $M = 0.6$; $N = 0.4$

19. One of the Hardy-Weinberg assumptions states that the population is infinitely large. What influence might small populations have on a Hardy-Weinberg equilibrium?

Answer: Sampling error would cause random and possibly significant fluctuations in gene frequencies.

20. One of the Hardy-Weinberg assumptions states that the population is free of selective advantage. What influence might selective advantage have on a Hardy-Weinberg equilibrium?

Answer: Certain genes will reach the next generation on a nonrandom basis, thus upsetting the equilibrium.

Sample Questions: Chapter 22 Population Genetics

21. What is meant by the symbolism $p + q = 1.0$?

Answer: The sum of the relevant individual alleles in a population is equal to 100 % of those alleles.

22. What does the expression *2pq* represent?

Answer: the frequency of heterozygotes for a given allelic pair

23. Assuming that $p = 0.3$ for a population, what would be the expected frequency of heterozygotes for the involved allelic pair?

Answer: 0.42

24. Give a brief definition of the term *genetic equilibrium*.

Answer: A population is in genetic equilibrium when the frequency of a given gene remains constant from generation to generation.

25. A certain form of color blindness in humans is sex-linked. Assume that 8 % of the males in a population is color blind. What percentage of the females in this population is expected to be color blind?

Answer: 0.64%

26. What is the original source of genetic variation in a population? What natural factors reshuffle this original variation?

Answer: Mutation is the original source, while chromosomal assortment and crossing over reshuffle mutations.

27. Suppose that a given gene undergoes a mutation to its dominant allele such that two out of 100,000 offspring exhibit the new mutant phenotype. Assuming that these offspring are heterozygous, what is the mutation rate for the gene?

Answer: 1/100,000

28. Migration occurs when individuals move between populations. Considering a single pair of alleles, *A* and *a*, what formula is used to indicate the new frequency of *A* in one generation of migration?

Answer: $p_i = (1-m)p_i + mp_m$

Sample Questions: Chapter 22 Population Genetics

29. Mutation and migration introduce new alleles into populations. What is the principal force that shifts allelic frequencies within large populations?

Answer: natural selection

30. What term is given to the probability that a particular phenotype will survive and leave offspring?

Answer: fitness

31. The difference between fitness of a given genotype and another genotype considered as optimal is called the selection coefficient(s). What is the selection coefficient for a genotype (*aa*) when 99 of every 100 organisms successfully reproduce?

Answer: $s = 0.01$

32. Which is more significant in changing gene frequencies, selection against a dominant gene or selection against a recessive gene?

Answer: selection against a dominant gene

33. What is meant by *inbreeding depression*? How is the degree of populational heterozygosity related to the degree of inbreeding?

Answer: Inbreeding depression is the reduction in viability that often develops as an organism becomes homozygous for a high proportion of its genes. Inbreeding increases homozygosity.

34. In extreme cases, genetic drift may lead to the chance fixation of one allele to the _____ of another.

Answer: exclusion

35. What is the term for a measure of the loss of fitness caused by inbreeding?

Answer: inbreeding depression

36. Provide a simple definition of *inbreeding*.

Answer: Inbreeding is a form of nonrandom mating between blood relatives.

37. What are the genetic consequences of inbreeding?

Answer: For a given allele, inbreeding increases the proportion of homozygotes in a population.

38. In zoo animals, inbreeding often occurs because there is a lack of a sufficient pool of breeding individuals. Under such conditions, what characteristics often attend inbred organisms?

Answer: higher frequency of aberrant phenotypes and higher mortality rates

True/False Format

39. If a gene has three alleles in a population, their frequencies must add up to 1.5.

Answer: False

40. In the case of complete dominance, we cannot tell which individuals are homozygous dominants and which are heterozygous, but by knowing the frequency of the homozygous recessives, we can estimate the frequency of homozygous dominant and heterozygous genotypes.

Answer: True

41. Inbreeding by itself can change gene frequencies.

Answer: False

42. Genetic drift is primarily associated with relatively small breeding populations.

Answer: True

43. Mutations are regarded as a strong evolutionary mechanism for changing allelic frequencies.

Answer: False

44. Given an inheritance pattern of incomplete dominance and 81 flowers are red (R^1R^1), 18 flowers are pink (R^1R^2), and 1 flower is white (R^2R^2), the frequency of the R^1 allele is 0.9.

Answer: True

45. Selection is the differential reproduction of genotypes, resulting from their variable fitness.

Answer: True

Sample Questions: Chapter 22 Population Genetics

46. Regarding the calculation of gene frequencies in a population, $p + q = 1.0$.

Answer: True

47. In large random mating populations, random genetic drift is usually a significant factor in changing gene frequencies.

Answer: False

48. In *directional selection,* both phenotypic extremes are equally selected against.

Answer: False

Chapter 23

Multiple Choice Format

1. A number of mechanisms operate to maintain genetic diversity in a population. Why?

      A.   Homozygosity is an evolutionary advantage.
      B.   Diversity leads to inbreeding advantages.
      C.   Diversity may better adapt a population to inevitable changes in the environment.
      D.   Greater genetic diversity increases the chances of haploidy.
      E.   Genetic diversity helps populations avoid diploidy.

Answer: C

2. What term is applied to proteins produced by alleles producing slightly differing electrophoretic forms of proteins with apparently identical functions?

      A.   allozyme
      B.   heteroduplex
      C.   hybrid duplex
      D.   allelic segregation
      E.   protoenzyme

Answer: A

3. What method is often used to separate proteins and nucleic acids when estimating genetic variation in populations?

      A.   electrophoresis
      B.   centrifugation
      C.   absorption spectrophotometry
      D.   fluorometry
      E.   *in situ* hybridization

Answer: A

Sample Questions: Chapter 23 Genetics and Evolution

4. What is the term for a form of speciation in which one species gives rise to two distinct daughter species?

      A.   phyletic evolution
      B.   race diversification
      C.   cladogenesis
      D.   allopatric speciation
      E.   punctuated evolution

Answer: C

5. What is the general term used to group various biological and behavioral properties of organisms that act to prevent or reduce interbreeding?

      A.   phyletic evolution
      B.   allopatric speciation
      C.   reproductive isolating mechanisms
      D.   inbreeding
      E.   genetic divergence

Answer: C

Short Answer Format

6. Richard Lewontin has estimated that about _____ of all loci are polymorphic. In any individual within that group, about _____ of the loci exhibit genetic variation in the form of heterozygosity.

Answer: two-thirds, one-third

7. Genetic diversity can be assessed at a variety of levels: DNA sequences, proteins, and chromosomes. Briefly describe methods that are currently used to assess diversity at each of the levels mentioned.

Answer: Differences in DNA sequences are often determined by reassociation kinetics (C_{ot} values) or sometimes by direct DNA sequencing. Differences in amino acids are often determined by electrophoresis and direct sequencing of proteins. Variations in the karyotype (inversions, translocations, fusions, etc.) often are used to reveal evolutionary change.

Sample Questions: Chapter 23 Genetics and Evolution

8. Present a rationale for using DNA sequence polymorphisms as an index of genetic diversity. Is genetic diversity directly proportional to evolutionary (phylogenetic) diversity?

Answer: It is natural to expect that the forces that bring about speciation are dependent upon reproductive isolation. As groups of organisms become reproductively isolated (whether through development of geographic or genetic barriers), it is natural to expect that through the accumulation of mutations, DNA sequences will diverge. It is also natural to expect that some DNA sequences will diverge more rapidly than others and that some differences in DNA sequences may be more evolutionarily important than others. Therefore, while there may be a general relationship between genetic diversity and evolutionary (phylogenetic) diversity, it is likely that there are exceptions.

9.   What is meant by the term *stasis* in an evolutionary sense?

Answer: Stasis is the condition in which for a relatively long period of time, a species does not appear to change.

10.   How is the degree of populational homozygosity related to the degree of inbreeding?

Answer: Inbreeding depression is the reduction in viability that often develops as an organism becomes homozygous for a high proportion of its genes. Inbreeding increases homozygosity.

11.   What is meant, in an evolutionary sense, by *phyletic evolution* or *anagenesis*?

Answer: Anagenesis occurs when a species undergoes a period of steady transformation.

12.   Why are some proteins more likely to diverge within a species than some other proteins?

Answer: Slowly evolving proteins are usually those that are necessary for cellular or organismic survival. Proteins that have little influence on survival are more likely to accommodate amino acid changes.

13. Why do SSU rRNAs provide insight into broad evolutionary relationsips?

Answer: Base changes in such RNAs are usually correlated with phylogenetic divergence, and these RNAs are highly conserved because they are under strong functional constraint.

Sample Questions: Chapter 23 Genetics and Evolution

14. Why is mitochondrial DNA often used in the construction of phylogentic trees?

Answer: Mitochondrial DNA evolves relatively quickly so that if a "fast clock" is needed to estimate relatively short evolutionary time periods, mitochondrial DNA can be especially useful.

15. Present generalities regarding phylogeny and genome size.

Answer: Nuclear DNA content increases from less to more complex organisms. Similar amounts of DNA usually, although not always, exist among closely related species. DNA content among terrestrial vertebrates is reduced when compared to other vertebrates.

16. What type of information can be gained by examining the amino acid sequence of a protein like cytochrome c?

Answer: Cytochrome c is a respiratory pigment found in the mitochondria of eukaryotes. Because of its vital role in aerobic metabolism it has evolved very slowly. Differences signify vast evolutionary distances.

17. Cytochrome c is a respiratory pigment found in the mitochondria of eukaryotes. Compared to some other proteins, it has changed very slowly over long periods of time. Why?

Answer: It serves a vital function; therefore, any changes in amino acid sequence are usually strongly selected against.

18. What are *phylogenetic trees*?

Answer: Phylogenetic trees are representations of evolutionary relationships among organisms.

19. In what way might molecular hybridization be used to infer phylogenetic relationships?

Answer: Differences in thermal stability of DNA hybrids can be used to determine DNA relatedness.

20. Would one expect a linear relationship between DNA sequence divergence and phylogenetic distance?

Answer: Not necessarily; some sections of DNA have much more influence on phylogenetic divergence than other sections.

21. What information has mitochondrial DNA offered concerning the phylogeneic relationships between Neanderthals and humans?

Answer: Although Neanderthals and humans share a common ancestor, Neanderthals were a separate hominid line and did not contribute mitochondrial genes to *H. sapiens*.

22. Provide a general definition for the term *speciation*.

Answer: the process of splitting a genetically homogeneous population into two or more populations that undergo genetic differentiation and eventual reproductive isolation

23. What are common factors in the speciation process?

Answer: The generation of reproductive isolating mechanisms; geographic, behavioral, physiological, and mechanical are common factors in the speciation process.

24. What is meant by the term *molecular clock*?

Answer: Molecular clocks are amino acid or nucleic acid sequences in which evolutionary changes accumulate over time. Ideally, such changes accumulate at a constant rate.

25. How does *parsimony* relate to studies of evolutionary biology?

Answer: In evolutionary studies based on parsimony, phylogenetic trees are developed on the minimum number of evolutionary changes and the simplest possible tree.

26. Which of the following nucleotide sequences would one expect to evolve the slowest: microsatellites or rRNA? Explain.

Answer: One would expect rRNA to evolve the slowest because it is involved in the structure of ribosomes. Ribosome structure must be highly conserved to ensure fidelity of protein synthesis.

27. Why would one expect cytochrome c to evolve slowly?

Answer: Cytochrome c is involved with energy production through the electron transport chain. Because cellular respiration is a fundamental process of aerobes, it is highly conserved and therefore subject to considerable selective constraints.

True/False Format

28. Natural selection occurs when there is nonrandom elimination of individuals from a population.

Answer: True

Sample Questions: Chapter 23 Genetics and Evolution

29. Inversion heterozygotes may reduce genetic variation by reducing the passage of recombinant gametes.

Answer: True

30. It is possible that a base substitution in DNA may have no phenotypic consequence.

Answer: True

31. Evolution is dependent on genetic diversity in the evolving population.

Answer: True

32. The conservation of an amino acid sequence among distantly related groups of organisms is suggestive of an important function of that sequence.

Answer: True

33. Relatively speaking, cytochrome c and histone genes evolve very rapidly.

Answer: False

34. VNTR sequence lengths are highly conserved among all mammals.

Answer: False

35. Traditionally, in malarial-infested areas of the world, there is selection for the sickle-cell gene.

Answer: True

36. With an endangered species, saving the species will guarantee the restoration of the genetic variation that originally existed among members of that species.

Answer: False

Chapter 24

Multiple Choice Format

1. The variation represented by plants and animals is known as

    A. biodiversity.
    B. conservation.
    C. evolutionary heterosis.
    D. contract digression.
    E. none of the above.

Answer: A

2. At what levels do most scientists examine genetic diversity?

    A. species and kingdom
    B. female and male
    C. interspecific and intraspecific
    D. species A and species B
    E. higher and lower forms

Answer: C

3. The U.S. Food and Agriculture Organization (FAO) estimated that as of 1990, _____ % of the genetic diversity in agricultural crops has been lost.

    A. 50
    B. 20
    C. 30
    D. 90
    E. 75

Answer: E

Sample Questions: Chapter 24 Conservation Genetics

4. Interspecific diversity refers to

    A.   diversity between species.
    B.   diversity within species.
    C.   diversity within a particular population.
    D.   diversity within an individual.
    E.   diversity within an isolated population.

Answer: A

5. The shrinking of available habitat reduces populations of wild species and often also isolates them from each other. Individual populations become trapped in pockets of undeveloped land surrounded by areas of agriculture. This process is called

    A.   isolation.
    B.   stagnation.
    C.   overdevelopment.
    D.   underdevelopment.
    E.   population fragmentation.

Answer: E

6. Predominantly inbreeding species, such as those that self-fertilize, tend to have greater levels of _____ than _____ diversity, respectively.

    A.   interpopulation, intrapopulation
    B.   isopopulation, gametopopulation
    C.   intrapopulation, interpopulation
    D.   specific, interspecific
    E.   nonmutant, mutant

Answer: A

7. What two experimental techniques are used to reveal AFLPs (amplified fragment length polymorphisms)?

    A.   centrifugation and PCR
    B.   restriction digestion and complementation
    C.   Southern and northern blotting
    D.   restriction digestion and PCR
    E.   electrophoresis and centrifugation

Answer: B

Sample Questions: Chapter 24 Conservation Genetics

8. What is an isozyme?

    A.   multiple versions of a single enzyme in a species
    B.   multiple genes in a chromosome
    C.   variations that are lethal in homozygotes
    D.   variations that give a selective advantage in the heterozygous state
    E.   multiple forms of mitochondrial DNA

Answer: A

Short Answer Format

9. What is meant by the *effective population size* (N_e)?

Answer: The effective population size is defined as the number of individuals in a population having an equal probability of contributing gametes to the next generation.

10. What is meant by the *absolute population size* (N)?

Answer: The absolute population size is the total number of individuals in the population.

11. Briefly describe what is meant by a population bottleneck.

Answer: Bottlenecks occur when a population or species is reduced to a few reproducing individuals whose offspring then increase in numbers over subsequent generations to reestablish the population.

12. After a population or species experiences a bottleneck, what might be expected in terms of biodiversity in the survivors?

Answer: biodiversity will be reduced

13. When a new population, derived from a small subset of individuals, has significantly less genetic diversity than the original population, it is said to be exhibiting a
_____.

Answer: founder effect

Sample Questions: Chapter 24 Conservation Genetics

14. When the number of breeding individuals is small, there is a high likelihood of genetic drift. One probable result is _____.

Answer: fixation of alleles

15. What is measured by the *inbreeding coefficient (F)*?

Answer: The inbreeding coefficient measures the probability that two alleles of a given gene in an individual are derived from a common ancestral gene.

16. Briefly describe the common negative aspect of inbreeding depression.

Answer: loss of heterozygosity and an increased homozygosity of deleterious alleles

17. The number of deleterious alleles present in the gene pool of a population is referred to as the _____.

Answer: genetic load

18. The gradual exchange of alleles between two populations, brought about by the dispersal of gametes or the migration of individuals is called _____.

Answer: gene flow

19. The loss of previously existing genetic diversity from a population or a species is referred to as _____.

Answer: genetic erosion

20. Briefly describe the difference between *ex situ* conservation and *in situ* conservation.

Answer: *Ex situ* conservation involves the removal of organisms from their original habitat to an artificially maintained location, while *in situ* conservation deals with organisms in their original habitat.

Sample Questions: *Chapter 24 Conservation Genetics*

21. The strategy of boosting numbers of organisms in a declining population by transplantation of the same species collected from more numerous populations elsewhere is called_____.

Answer: population augmentation

22. Describe a potential problem associated with population augmentation.

Answer: *Outbreeding depression* can occur because the progeny of crosses between the native and introduced species may be less fit for the native environment.

True/False Format

23. Interspecific diversity and intraspecific diversity provide an assessment of essentially identical parameters.

Answer: False

24. Genetic variation with populations can be measured as the frequency of individuals in the population that are heterozygous at a given locus, or as the number of different alleles at a locus that are present in the gene pool.

Answer: True

25. *Population fragmentation* results from conditions that reduce habitats and trap individual populations in undeveloped land surrounded by areas of developed land.

Answer: True

26. Intrapopulation genetic diversity increases under prolonged conditions of population fragmentation.

Answer: False

27. DNA profiles can be used to detect and quantify genetic differences between individuals.

Answer: True

Sample Questions: Chapter 24 Conservation Genetics

28. AFLPs (amplified fragment length polymorphisms) allow DNA profiling through the use of restriction enzymes and PCR.

Answer: True

29. DNA fingerprinting can be applied to problems involving endangered species because, with the DNA fingerprint, systems of migration, breeding, and heterozygosity can be assessed.

Answer: True

30. Isozyme analysis allows an investigator an opportunity to determine the sequence of a particular stretch of DNA.

Answer: False

31. The *effective population size* is usually greater than the *absolute population size*.

Answer: False

32. Population bottlenecks are generally beneficial to a species because they provide an opportunity to weed out weaker alleles.

Answer: False

33. Inbreeding usually increases heterozygosity of specific genes in a population.

Answer: False

34. The founder effect generally results in an increase in heterozygosity.

Answer: False

35. Genetic drift usually leads to a loss of genetic variation.

Answer: True